Praise for *OOF*

"Sometimes sad and sometimes hilarious, Witherspoon's timely metafictional novel explores the ways (mis)information can shape public discourse in the digital media age ...the wildly entertaining result illuminates the dark side to fame, circa 2021."

— *BookLife by Publishers Weekly*

"An innovative literary experiment that supplies thoughtful commentary on the 'discourse virus' of our age ...Witherspoon tackles a broad spectrum of media, including comically scathing excerpts from tweets, podcasts, blogs, and even academic journals and also keenly exposes the ways in which Strobe, the character, is implicated in his own online assault, due to his obsessive attachment to public life."

— *Kirkus Reviews*

"an impressive achievement of unflinching honesty from a noteworthy talent, as resonant and relevant as it is entertaining ...OOF tugs at the threads that connect American cynicism with radical extremism and weaves a character-rich tapestry of insight ...Each voice, whether of a *New Yorker* journalist or an Internet influencer, is rendered with uncanny fidelity. Perhaps most masterful is that key events are not depicted but merely alluded to, occurring off-camera between entries, allowing the text to provide an elegant framework for a more personal story painted almost invisibly in the negative space."

— *BlueInk Review*

"a work of pure creative genius, engaging and thought-provoking ...You know you are in for a treat when an author makes fun of himself, as Witherspoon wears two hats as an inquisitor general and heretic at the same time."

— *Readers' Favorite*

"Those interested in "the low art of chronicling human stupidity" will not be able to put this book down ...Fans of works like *Dear Committee Members* will immediately find a new favorite in this book, as well as a new type of unlikely hero in Strobe Witherspoon."

— *US Review of Books*

# OOF

a novel

by
## Strobe Witherspoon

*For my dear son Mitchell*

# 1

# FLOTUS: A Memoir

Preface

People always ask me how he smelled. It's an invasive question. And insulting. As if he smelled really bad, and that was evidence I was just with him for the money.

For the record, he smelled good. Like fresh dry-cleaning mixed with buttery sunscreen. That smell told me that he was well put together, that he cared about his presentation and about putting his best foot forward. It was always there, that smell: when I first met him, when we ate breakfast, when he came into my bedroom late at night (if he wasn't too tired).

He got excited by shiny things. I've always liked shiny things; they remind me of the baroque architecture of my homeland. But I had never met anyone with such a carnivorous appetite for shine, and it excited me.

Everyone responded to his charm. Even when he was making people do things they didn't want to do. "It's gonna be so good for you. So stop with the hemming, the hawing, and approve da project already," he told people over meals of steak and cake.

"Weren't you just arm candy?" people ask.

No! We were a team.

He would put his long arms around me after a successful dinner with a community board member or some other person he needed something from, and he would whisper, "You were the reason they said yes. The questions about his daughter's recital ... perfect."

They *were* perfect questions. I always found a way to get people talking about something in their personal life that they cared about.

"The higher up you get, the more people come after you," he told me.

People came after him all the time. And that made him mad (and a little excited). I knew that sometimes he probably deserved it, that he could have been a little more accommodating. But what did it matter? If he were nicer, they would have just taken more from us and never stopped taking until all the shine was gone. He believed that. So did I, eventually.

For me, however, the lifestyle became something I didn't want. I was getting older. I was tired of the eyes always on us—always nitpicking me, our relationship, our children, our business.

But he was *so* much older, and he didn't want out. So, first it was the separate bedrooms. Then the long stretches at different homes.

Distance became the norm.

That started to change when he ran for office. And when he told me to stop having nude models over for my painting class. And when Leif, my assistant, started to "advise" me about my dietary habits and facial expressions in public.

I had grown too comfortable in his absence, I told myself. I needed to get back to being that person at the dinners (minus the cake consumption). But it was difficult. I now enjoyed painting, philosophy, history. Not smiling, waving, starving.

When my gallery show was canceled just before the presidential primaries, I cried. I also cried when the gallery sued us. And when they took my paintings hostage until we paid.

We never paid.

I think it made him happy. My life's passion had been extinguished.

"Can't you get your lawyers to go after the gallery like you normally do?" I asked him.

"I'll get to it," he responded.

He didn't get to it. I should be around for more events, he must have decided. More speeches. More chanting.

But I'm not a violent person.

Too much has already been written about that. I will not profess my innocence again. Not in this book, not to strangers on the street, and not to another law enforcement official.

I want people to see the other side of me, the immigrant who speaks five languages. Who just got her second master's degree. Who is bursting with creativity and compassion for her fellow Americans.

I want to be the bridge between the tragedy of our country's recent past and the promise of the future. I know it will be hard. Our wounds are fresh. Our debts, to the banks and to each other, are coming due.

Blame is not the answer. We must embrace this moment. Mine it for opportunities for inspiration, both personal and national.

I have pushed myself to be the most successful person I can be. That drive brought me all the way to the White House. It brought me to the country that I now call home—the country that beckons people like me from afar, tantalizing us with opportunity and freedom and liberty in exchange for hard work and unwavering commitment.

I have done a lot of things that I am proud of. I have done some things that I am not proud of. And I hope to do many more things in the future. This book is about all of that. This book is not about *him*. Yes, it will include stories about our time together. But it is not about *him*.

I hope you enjoy it.

# 2

# OOF: A Compendium

Introduction

W hen everything was happening, Strobe and I were in constant contact. One of the many projects we discussed was this compendium. We were both of the opinion that the current political climate was destroying our ability to engage in good-faith discourse about complicated issues. This compendium would be one small effort to catalog and expose this discourse virus, allowing historians of tomorrow to better understand its transmission and prevent its future proliferation.

But now Strobe is gone. All I have left of him is this project and the memories of his unwavering commitment to the low art of chronicling human stupidity.

He was a simple man, always late or canceling. Terribly dressed, usually wearing an ill-fitting T-shirt that read something like "Your With Stupid." If he was lucky, he could rope someone into this exchange:

"It should say 'y-o-u-apostrophe-r-e with stupid.'"

"It should say what?"

"'Y-O-U-APOSTROPHE-R-E WITH STUPID. You're with stupid'!"

Strobe would smirk and put his hand on his mark's shoulder. "C'mon, don't sell yourself short."

It was never funny. Except to Strobe, to whom the human race's unrelenting idiocy brought great joy. He was in his mid-forties but openly fantasized about being older, of an age that no longer required him to explain or justify his hermit-like existence. He abhorred parades, offices, or anywhere with a lot of people.

"Business is good because things are bad," he once told me. "As the human race lurches from one horrendous calamity to the next, I'll be there."

His audience's appreciation afforded him a lifestyle of snarky solitude that I must admit I envied. Every year since graduate school, I was writing more and earning less. Strobe, I could tell, felt bad for me. Which is why I thought he might just be humoring me about this project. Or worse, pitying me—letting me feel like this book would be my lasting contribution to society, the thing that people would remember me for (as opposed to the reality show episode recaps or the in-flight magazine profiles that were my stock and trade). Maybe he was just lazy and wanted me to do the work.

But not all of his audience was there to applaud. His detractors' appetite for destruction was insatiable. These people, many of whom were running internet surpluses/human-interaction deficits, stopped at nothing to destroy everything that Strobe built. They made him the centerpiece of a story so batshit crazy that a fictionalized version wouldn't do it justice. Hence, the compendium.

This book won't bring Strobe back. It won't stop our society's sprint to the bottom—a sprint that would be hilarious if it weren't so real.

But unlike my other stalled projects, I feel compelled by

a force larger than me to see this one to its completion. So, behold: *OOF: A Compendium.*

This collection is intended to capture the essence of the Online Outrage Fiesta (OOF) that led to my friend's demise. It will be diverse in its sources—news articles, blog posts, tweet storms, emails, transcripts, etc. It will also try to incorporate perspectives from across the fringe-mainstream and left-right spectrums. This approach will hopefully provide you, the reader, with a sense of the toxic ingredients that poisoned Strobe Witherspoon's well.

Where necessary, I provide commentary to contextualize and correct the record, but I (mostly) refrain from editorializing. In some instances, I edited for brevity. Sometimes, I aggregated and summarized the totality of contributing writers and organizations. In a few cases, I thought it best to use individual authors multiple times to create continuity, add depth, and shed light on the larger movements they were connected to.

This book will provide interested readers of the future with a road map for understanding how narratives can snowball into something utterly unrecognizable from the original snowflake. (Can I still use that word?) More importantly, this book will show how outrage on the internet can turn into real-world damage that can't be deleted.

In *FLOTUS: A Memoir*, the preface ends with, "I hope you enjoy it."

I'm inclined to say something similar here. But then again, maybe enjoyment is the problem. Maybe if you enjoy it, you're part of the problem. Or if you don't enjoy it, you will come after me on the internet. Which may also be part of the problem. Regardless, here it is. I wish it had a better ending.

# Witherspoon's Latest Sparks Bidding War

Publishers Weekly

**Forsythe Edwards** at Stein, Latham, and Latham imprint VITAL Books acquired North American and first serial rights to **Strobe Witherspoon's** *FLOTUS: A Memoir* for $850,000– Witherspoon's biggest advance to date. *FLOTUS* is a fictional tale of one woman's rise from humble Slovakian beginnings to First Lady of the United States (FLOTUS). Industry interest was strong, based on growing recognition of Witherspoon's magazine pieces and previous books (*furtl, Hell Is Other People's Instagram and Other Short Stories*). Additionally, fiction and nonfiction works about the last White House administration, not to mention FLOTUS biographies, remain industry bright spots for writers of all political persuasions. Witherspoon is represented by **Dan Manson** at Miller/Thyme Literary Agency.

# Leaked Chapter of FLOTUS Novel Raises Questions

The New Journal

*Publishers Weekly* recently reported on the sale of yet another book about the last president and his inner circle. In *FLOTUS: A Memoir*, Strobe Witherspoon, a self-proclaimed radical provocateur, tries to get inside the head of a first lady who sounds strikingly similar to the last FLOTUS.

### Has Witherspoon Gone Too Far?

*The New Journal* has exclusively obtained the preface to *FLOTUS*, available to our premium subscribers. In these pages, the authenticity of which has been confirmed by a source close to the author, the fictional FLOTUS briefly refers to an "incident." There has been speculation that this is a not-so-veiled reference to a foiled attack on the president that occurred in real life. Questions around the first lady's role in that poorly executed scheme have only increased since her recent announcement that she filed for divorce from her husband—the first time any president, current or former, had been served such papers—and will no longer be using his last name.

The former first lady had no comment when contacted by the Journal.

# Liberty Lisa's
# Victory Vlog #285

---

Transcript

---

[LLVV LOGO INTRO]

**LL:** Hi guys, welcome back. First off, thanks so much for your donations last week. We were able to rescue three adorable doggies from some truly terrible situations in Los Angeles. I don't even want to describe it. Too heartbreaking. How can people be so cruel? Our cities are a cesspool!

Speaking of cruelty, have you seen this book about the former first lady? If you haven't, let me summarize. Some irrelevant Massachusetts elitist by the name of Strobe Witherspoon has decided to weigh in on what is unequivocally a private matter—the marital standing of our beloved former president and his soon-to-be ex-wife. Just another chapter in the mainstream media's nonstop hate-filled bile carnival for our generation's Ronald Reagan.

# OOF

But it gets worse. Way. Freakin'. Worse.

[GOLDEN RETRIEVER PASSES THROUGH FRAME]

Not only does this "fictional" memoir claim to speak for the former first lady's innermost thoughts, but it weighs in on and fans the flame of a long-debunked conspiracy theory.

Look, I'm no constitutional lawyer, but this is not speech that is protected by the First Amendment, as the courts have clearly stipulated for decades. Twitter trolls have been visited by the feds for less than this.

And, c'mon. The references in these leaked chapters are just sooooooo obvious. "Steak and Cake"? "Slovakia"? This third-rate attention grab reeks of the last dying death belch of a writer with no original thoughts and nothing productive to contribute to society.

The nerve of this godless fool. Exploiting the deep division within our country for personal gain. Our country needs to heal right now. Not poke fun.

I have some additional information about this soon-to-be-published presidential smear campaign masquerading as literary fiction. And I'm gonna give my gold subscription members some exclusive content that you can't get anywhere else.

Reportedly, in newly surfaced chapters of the book—other than the preface—*FLOTUS* engages in downright disgusting and deviant sexual behavior at the behest of her husband.

I'm talkin' D-V-ENT.

Apparently the "fictional" president in this book likes it when FLOTUS—how can I say this nicely?—attaches a contraption that allows her to take on the role of the male, while the president is reportedly dressing and acting in a manner more appropriate for a female. Not the kind of family values I was raised with, that's for sure. Totally undermines the integrity of the office of the president.

What is going on in America? Do they think that we all want to live in San Francisco, where welfare queens buy sirloin steaks and tech nerds pretend to care from their fancy gated mansions on a hill?

And there's more! In the chapters leaked to me—exclusively—there are details regarding FLOTUS's relationship with a shady crime syndicate.

These chapters seem almost a little too detailed, if you know what I'm saying. Like maybe this hack Witherspoon knows more than he is letting on.

I'm not sure if this Strobetard is aware, but being an accessory to a presidential assassination is A CRIME!

So... let that sink in, Strobe.

[GOLDEN RETRIEVER ENTERS FRAME AND STARTS LICKING LISA'S FACE]

**LL:** Goldwater—stop that! Sorry, but this doggo is incorrigible!

Where was I? Oh yeah, the fire of justice burns strong in me. And I will not let this stand.

But I'll tell you what will stand. Strobe Witherspoon will stand... on trial!

I am calling on all my fellow patriots out there to boy-cott all related entities and stand with me in calling for the treasonous Strobe Witherspoon to be strung up for his treason. No More Treason Strobe!

[LLVV LOGO OUTRO]

# Should the Secret Service Pay a Visit to Strobe Witherspoon?

The Letter of the Law Blog—
where the Constitution reigns supreme

The English Treason Act of 1351 was established to make it a crime to "compass or imagine" the death of the king. Centuries later, this became the foundation for Sections 871 (for sitting presidents) and 879 (for former presidents) of US Code Title 18. This type of activity is a class E felony, with a penalty of up to five years in jail if a guilty verdict is reached.

Strobe Witherspoon, according to a number of commentators on the internet, has run afoul of one or both of these statutes. Calls for Witherspoon's arrest have been growing.

In this post, I will unpack some of the various legal theories on the matter and explore the nuance that may not be receiving the attention it deserves from the punditocracy.

In cases dealing with a threat made to a sitting or former president, most individuals investigated by the Secret

Service—approximately 75 percent—are deemed mentally ill. In those instances, the judicial system tends to refer defendants to the necessary mental health institutions to assess their threat to society and themselves.

For those that do not struggle with mental health issues, there is frequently a question of "seriousness" that must be assessed. Did it appear that the threat-maker was indicating even the slightest willingness to go through with such a threat? In cases where the answer is yes, jail time is not uncommon.

But what about cases where the threat comes in the guise of political hyperbole? In 1966, the Supreme Court ruled on the case of an eighteen-year-old who didn't want to join the army. He reportedly said:

> "And now I have already received my draft classification as 1-A and I have got to report for my physical this Monday coming. I am not going. If they ever make me carry a rifle the first man I want to get in my sights is [President] L.B.J."

The courts did not see his rhetoric as either treasonous by itself or something that "arouses resentment and concern on the part of patriotic citizens." He was not punished.

Witherspoon's case appears to push the boundaries of this precedent and intersects with earlier concerns about not just the personal intent inherent in one's speech, but the impact of this speech on those that consume it, particularly the mentally unstable. The US Attorney's Manual entry on this subject stipulates that apprehension about the mentally ill extends beyond their potential to pursue this activity unprovoked: "The Secret Service is particularly concerned that media attention given to cases involving threats against protectees [i.e., sitting presidents and former presidents] may provoke violent acts from such mentally unstable persons."

This is where this situation starts to put Witherspoon in jeopardy. While one may argue that a threat or assassination "imagining," by way of a fictional work of literature, delivered by a person of sound mind, was done in jest or in a hyperbolic manner, one must still assess the potential for provocation from individuals that may not possess such light-hearted intentions or mental stability. Additionally, if there is evidence to support claims that Witherspoon has additional knowledge of a potential follow-up assassination plot from the suspected perpetrators, and that Witherspoon is in fact writing about it, and thereby potentially signaling to said perpetrators how to do it or triggering other mentally unstable individuals to pursue this activity, then he should expect to be punished to the full extent of the law.

In sum, the seriousness of the threat to our republic is so high that the authors of this law intentionally set the legal bar low to dissuade even those commenting on such heinous acts in a whimsical or irreverent manner. Additionally, considering the fraught, tense times we live in, one could argue that the legal bar should be even lower to avoid even the slightest potential for a cascade of events that could put any of our commanders-in-chief, current or former, in harm's way.

Ergo, there can be no mistaking the legal jeopardy that Witherspoon now finds himself in. I suspect the Secret Service is discussing this situation with him at this very moment, as would be warranted by existing precedent and mainstream legal interpretation.

# RITATWEETZ1999

Tweet Storm

1/ these @strobewither sample chapters – I have thoughts. Lotsa thoughts.

2/ Fine not fine this rich white dude with an IMPOSSIBLY WASPY NAME calls himself a "radical provocateur". WHAT DOES THAT EVEN MEAN? Nothing radical nor provocateury about his outdated schtick. if you gotta call yourself that, U AINT THAT.

3/ Oh and STROBE stop trying to humanize a woman that has done more to set back the feminist movement than any woman this millennium. Not cool. Not helpful

4/ Her unwillingness to stand up for women is... #problematic.

5/ now we supposed 2 just sit back and applaud when STROBE writes about a "fictional" character he knows nothing about in an attempt to stay relevant. #SMDH #SWPD

6/ Some of us deserve a voice. Let's talk about my parent's immigrant story perhaps? Or how they r putting me through college with nothing. Where's that book? Oh yeah, I wrote it (available on Amazon link in bio)

7/ Can't STROBE just write about some clam chowder scandal of '78 where Cherston and Nathanial came to blows over the creaminess of some soup in a bread bowl? #ursweetspot

8/ Or what about when @LLBEAN ended their policy of eternal returns on all items? I seriously want to know what you think about that

9/ Ur no ally ol man. End Rant.

# The Case of Strobe Witherspoon

Nerdlaw Blog

In response to recent inquiries regarding sections 871 and 879 of US Code Title 18, I have compiled a short overview on the legal justification for calls for the prosecution of one Strobe Witherspoon. As a scholar who has spent the majority of my academic career studying extra-judicial assassination in international and domestic law contexts, I hope to be able to elucidate and remedy some of the misconceptions currently circulating around this news story. I will do this by drawing from primary historical sources as well as current legal norms and jurisprudence.

After exploring various arguments, I have come to a general conclusion I will summarize below, followed by a series of sub-conclusions that bolster my top-level argument.

Conclusion: This. Is. Bullshit.

Sub-conclusion 1: You partisan hacks are full of shit.

Sub-conclusion 2: This is the kind of baseless dog shit of an argument that is destroying civic and legal discourse in this country.

Sub-conclusion 3: Even taking the time to write this out has made me dumber. We are all dumber for participating in this shit parade.

There is no legal precedent that even comes close to justifying recourse against an author of this type of fiction under US Code Title 18, sections 871 or 879. For further evidence, please see the preponderance of political thrillers that "imagine" the assassination of a sitting president, many of which bear striking resemblances to real presidents. The only difference with this book is the hyper-partisan political environment we live in, where everyone is an expert and no one gives a crap about nuance. That is not a compelling legal argument for prosecution, in my humble opinion.

Secondly, it is nothing short of legal malpractice to weigh in on something like this on the internet without having even a basic understanding of the details of the case. To all budding lawyers out there: unsubstantiated rumors about book chapters that may not exist don't hold up in a court of law.

Thirdly, these types of attempts to use the legal system to improperly squash the creative pursuits of people we disagree with threaten the basic foundations upon which this country was founded. It's called the First Amendment. Look it up, internet detectives.

Now, please stop emailing me.

PS: Don't forget to check out my forthcoming novel, *Terminate with Extreme Prejudice*, book 2 of the Hilton Grimes Crimes of Political Passion series. Preorders from this website get a 15% discount and a signed bookmark (friendly reminder: Nerdlaw blog + adjunct professoring ≠ living wage).

# Witherspoon Announcement Mired by Controversy

The New York Times

This was supposed to be a celebratory moment for author Strobe Witherspoon. His new novel, *FLOTUS: A Memoir*, sold for just below a million dollars after a bidding war broke out.

Just as soon as it was announced, questions about the plot emerged. Witherspoon's book references the recently uncovered plot against the previous US President. Outrage and speculation over this real-world incident have filled the airwaves in recent months.

Some have suggested that this outrage was part of Witherspoon's plan from the outset. His former work as a researcher at the CIA has also led to speculation that he has access to information that is not available to the general public. This claim has taken on a life of its own in certain conspiratorial communities on the internet. To date, however, there is no evidence to support said claim.

His critics argue that even if these theories are proven false, now is not the time for satirical stunts. "Strobe, this isn't the kind of humor that heals!" read one of many angry tweets directed at Witherspoon yesterday. "Our nation isn't in the mood, Strobet-rd!" read another.

Witherspoon has not responded to repeated requests for comment. His publisher, VITAL Books, released a statement, proclaiming their "unwavering support for Witherspoon" and his "mission to provide levity and catharsis in these challenging times." The publishing house also appears to be embracing the kind of book publicity that money can't buy: they have launched aggressive social media campaigns using the hashtags, #STANDSTRONGFORSTROBE and #THISWITHERSPOONWILLNOTWITHER.

The stakes couldn't be higher for this once-prominent imprint. Reports of financial challenges at VITAL have surfaced amid a number of high-profile disappointments, including the novel *I Was Drunk at the Time*, the nonfiction book *In Defense of R. Kelly*, and the adult-themed children's book *Poopie Smells Like Sh-t*.

On the horizon, challenges loom. Growing boycott calls could test VITAL's resolve, particularly since one of its most prominent authors is religious right-wing provocateur Carl Chenneworth. *Deep State Heathens* is the working title of his next book.

Chenneworth himself got into the act earlier this week, creating his own Twitter hashtags #STRONGLYAGAINSTSTROBE and #WITHERSPOONSHOULDWITHER. VITAL Books responded to Chenneworth's tweets, saying, "We respect all of our authors' freedom of speech. Lively debates of this nature are the cornerstone of a healthy democracy, and we are proud to play a small role in protecting this founding American principle."

In the coming days, this case will continue to work its way through the court of public opinion. As both sides dig in to their positions, a definitive verdict, however, may be elusive.

# This Will Not Stand

**by Strobe Witherspoon**

HellisOtherPeoplesBlogs.com

When I was a child, I used to steal. A lot. Like many klepto-
maniacs before me, it wasn't about the money. I didn't need
to steal that yellow Sony Sports Walkman in eighth grade; I
had a Walkman already. In high school, I didn't need to skim
from the cash register when I worked at the The Country's
Best Yogurt or take the gift cards and sell them to my friends.

I have nothing profound to say about my klepto phase. It was
about the rush and the power and impressing my friends. Or
just getting friends in the first place; because I was always
the new kid, stealing seemed like a nice and quick way to win
them over.

When I got caught, which happened more than a few times,
I was punished. Sometimes the punishments were embarrassing. Sometimes they were empowering. The girls took
notice. The boys thought I was tougher than I was.

# OOF

One time, I spent eight hours in a Bar Harbor jail. My friends and I had been crewing a sailboat for the summer, and things had gotten boring. Everyone else got away from the J. Scott Harriman Apparel security guard. I tripped on the boat shoes I had stolen (the tags were still on). When the security guard patted me down, he found ten tie clips with lobsters on them in my pocket.

As it turned out, those tie clips cost thirty-five dollars each. And the boat shoes, seventy-five dollars. In other words, my loot was worth over four hundred dollars. And that made it a felony.

When I found out, I started to tremble. There were going to be ramifications for my actions. I feared that my summer would be taking a turn for the worse.

I was correct: my mom made the three-hour drive south to pick me up, bail me out, and drive me home. It was a quiet ride.

There would be no more Bar Harbor hijinks, only mandatory book reports each week covering a different historical era; mowing all the yards in the cul-de-sac; and helping my brother, Wheeler, prepare for his dressage competitions. RIP Wheeler.

Why am I telling you this story? Because my actions had consequences. In retrospect, I recognize the causality and accept the outcome.

I do not have the same feelings today, as I look out into the sea of negativity that surrounds the sale of my recent satirical novel. The punishment does not fit the crime. The virtual spittle-infused rants from all corners of the internet are an affront to good-faith debates, and I reject them with every fiber of my being.

I'm all for constructive criticism. In fact, I enjoy it. But what is going on here is not that.

I can hear the responses now.

"But Strobe, what about you? You traffic in all sorts of outrageous content that can be mean-spirited and fallacious."

"But Strobe, who are you to tell me how to feel and express myself? Go back to whatever ascot-wearing apple orchard you crawled out of."

"But Strobe, not all of us have lucrative book deals and typewriters that were once owned by John Updike. This is how our voices can be heard. Adapt or die, Strobe."

Perhaps now would be a good time to lay out what it is that I do for a living. I am a writer. My most recent fiction has been focused on societal collapse and political malfeasance. It's frequently characterized as satirical, some of it dystopian. These are genres that I find comfort in—genres in which I can spin ridiculous yarns that test the bounds of my imagination, draw out the absurdity of modern life, and exorcise some of my frustrations with the social and political order of the day. I have no great affinity for any grand political ideologies, and I loathe dogmatic blowhards. I will confess, however, to being dogmatic about one thing: the indefatigable, unrelenting stupidity of the human race, of which I myself am

undoubtedly a member. Which I guess makes me a hypocrite. A stupid hypocrite, no less. But one with no shortage
of material to draw from.

Hopefully, my literary endeavors remind readers that they
are not alone in their societal disappointment. Perhaps my
work adds some levity during this otherwise gloomy moment
in history.

I realize that my work does not bring everybody joy. For
some, it feels like I am cashing in on tragic human flaws.
But—and this is an important *but*—the extrapolating that
goes on in my work is never intended to be taken literally
or seriously.

In fact, my worst moments as a writer have been when I have
taken myself too seriously. And if anybody reads *FLOTUS*
with an expectation that I will expose real facts about a real
person, they are going to be disappointed, and I sincerely
apologize for wasting their time.

To be clear, I have no access to classified government information. I don't come from a long line of Freemasons. My
family isn't part of a global cabal to rig the monetary system
for its own benefit.

Also, there is not, nor has there ever been, any passages
within the pages of *FLOTUS: A Memoir* that describe a fictional US president getting penetrated in any of his orifices
by a fictional first lady.

To put an even finer point on it: if you look to my novels
for clues about future real-world events of which I have

absolutely no knowledge or interest, you are an idiot. I feel sorry for you.

The idiots behind attacks on me are clearly more interested in sculpting a false narrative than generating productive discourse. This nonsense then takes hold in the minds of others who are eager to accept it and add their own layer of outrage on top of it, regardless of any evidence to the contrary. Add to this a level of relentless irreverence (aka snark) that is intended to debase and humiliate me, and you get an environment where shared understanding is not on the agenda; rather, deepened division is the only potential outcome.

In conclusion, my ridiculous ideas are openly and unapologetically ridiculous. Your ridiculous ideas are masquerading as thoughtful discourse. And these ideas are being communicated with a level of certainty that is completely unearned and either naïve or malicious (or both).

This is not productive. This is not satire.

You have been warned. Strobe will not abide such indignity.

THIS. WILL. NOT. STAND.

Warm regards,

"Ol' Man" Strobe Witherspoon

# Infodemic Virality:
## The Role of Epistemological
## Compartmentalization on Transmission Dynamics

The Journal of Sociocultural Epidemiology (JoSE)

*Infodemic: An excessive amount of information concerning a problem such that the solution is made more difficult.*

**Abstract:** Nascent interdisciplinary research in philosophy and public health involves the deployment of epidemiological tools to study epistemology. An early example of this is the foundational scholarship on emerging infectious infodemics (Riejkskopp et al., 2017). This paper will explore one of the core components of Riejkskopp's baseline phenomenon, epistemological compartmentalization—i.e., irreconcilable approaches to postulation and worldview construction within competing communities—and its growing impact on the American body politic.

We tracked the viral transmission of different narratives via community networks and isolated the drivers of epistemological compartmentalization. We discovered that narrative replication within discrete communities is frequently sparked by a "super-spreader," either an individual or media outlet with sufficient reach and community credibility. Once this happens, exponential replication occurs via a variety of separate informational nodes. At the same time, the rejection of these narratives in communities of different geographic or sociocultural background spawn counternarratives, which then experience similar exponential replication. The results of this study demonstrate that simultaneous virality of structurally irreconcilable narratives within intersecting communities in the United States contributes to epistemological compartmentalization. This early-stage research is intended to support the creation of interventions that can contain, mitigate, and suppress future infodemics.

# The Media Botched the Strobe Witherspoon Story: Is Our Industry Doomed?

**By Pat Gold**

The Atlantic

Last week, in a seemingly innocuous announcement from *Publishers Weekly*, it was announced that Strobe Witherspoon sold a novel to VITAL Books, an imprint of Stein, Latham, and Latham that specializes in quirky, genre-busting fare. VITAL's last real hit was five years ago—*The Worst Underachiever Ever* by Sturgill Nicholson.

Purchasing *FLOTUS: A Memoir* for just under a million dollars was a bet on a trendy but risky title—an irreverent meditation on the life of a former First Lady of the United States. Witherspoon was wading into lucrative and controversial waters, likely in the hopes of raising his profile and bolstering his bank account.

I came across Mr. Witherspoon last year after his first-person excoriation of the influencer economy went viral. His poor man's Hunter S. Thompson approach won him many fans and almost as many enemies, after he convinced some "mommy bloggers" to hawk a particularly questionable item billed as "the best photo app on the market for getting rid of your newborn's pesky love handles." Not exactly subtle, but very much in line with his recent novel.

None of this debacle should, therefore, be surprising. Of course, a writer like Strobe Witherspoon was going to write a satirical novel about a first lady's *maybe* attempt to kill her husband. Because of course, the media is going to eat it up and spew it out like the overstuffed buffet of outrage that it is. Much has been written on this subject already. The grossly dysfunctional relationship between the media and the former president is convulsing our society in plain sight. This person singlehandedly saved journalism by attacking journalism. His nonstop temper tantrums produce a bottomless pit of think pieces and hot takes. Which leads to more clicks. More subscriptions. More outrage. We get more media hysteria in one day than we saw in the years before he magically paraglided to his golf course podium to announce his candidacy.

There are other costs. We know that now. We are losing our ability to thoughtfully process and debate the issues of our time. Intrigue and scandal so thoroughly consume us that people who cover this industry—like me—are reduced to writing articles about whether we should be writing articles about this.

What's the alternative? Can we cut this scourge off at the source? Does *The New Journal*, the first mainstream outlet to publish excerpts from *FLOTUS*, bear particular responsibility for fueling the fire? And what about *The New York Times*, standard bearer of the media elite? Does it deserve criticism for breathlessly covering the news about *FLOTUS*, giving oxygen to the more speculative components while using a journalistic style that allows it to project neutrality?

On the other hand, taking the high road could make it worse, giving power to this debacle's more spurious participants— the trolls, click farmers, memers, sh-tposters, and headline butchers. These actors blithely perpetuate an environment of oversimplified mockery and rush to judgment without so much as an inkling of journalistic integrity.

And thus, the cycle continues.

To that end, what do we know about this specific outrage-a-thon? It appears to focus on a far-fetched notion that Strobe Witherspoon, because he worked for the US government two lifetimes ago, has connections and can therefore cobble together information to send signals to … someone? Who, exactly? A secret crime syndicate? Will Witherspoon look prescient and wise for predicting more crimes? Will that get him on more television shows so he can denounce all of us and our obsession with the outrage cycle?

These theories remain questionable, almost too ridiculous to consider. Sure, there are some tidbits of this story that are based in truth, as per usual. Internet detectives have managed to unearth classified documents from decades ago. Witherspoon did apparently mine some contacts from his previous career as an intelligence officer for his past screenplays. Should we be surprised that he did that? He was a liberal arts college graduate who got sucked into the

WASPy world of the US intelligence community like so many WASPs before him. That's not a terribly exciting story. It's a boy emulating the careers of those who came before him—including, reportedly, his father. The slightly unique hiccup in this story comes when that boy, unfulfilled by the daily grind of incognito Google searches and PowerPoint decks, bolted for more provocative pastures and used his résumé to sell himself first as a spy thriller screenwriter and then an irreverent social critic. And yet, the think pieces keep coming—including this one.

If we're lucky, reputable news institutions and thought leaders will feel compelled to respond to this piece. Maybe there will be a *mea culpa* from some of the perpetrators—we have had a few of those over the years. With luck, all this back-and-forth will make this article go viral, and I will survive the next round of layoffs. Or perhaps not, since this isn't the first time someone has pointed out this information pickle we are in.

In closing, here is a relevant suggestion from a colleague of mine who also weighed in on the troubled state of journalism in the internet age and, like me, longs for the days of yore: "Journalistic ethics held that if you didn't have the reporting to support a story, and if that story had the potential to hurt its subjects ... you didn't run the story. You kept reporting it, you let yourself get scooped, you accepted that speed is not the highest value. Otherwise, you were the trash press."*

---

\* https://www.theatlantic.com/ideas/archive/2019/01/media-must-learn-covington -catholic-story/581035/)

Yes, this may be wishful, outdated thinking, put forward by journalistic dinosaurs like me. But the sentiment remains. The status quo is destroying us. Articles like this are destroying us. Please share it.

# 13

**Editor's Note:** After Strobe's blog post, and after some articles were published that were critical of the media's overblown reaction to Strobe's novel, things died down, cooler heads prevailed, and Strobe was able to focus on his next writing project.

Just kidding.

# Memes

- A picture of a manic Mel Gibson with a shaved head. The caption reads: "When you realize your book publicity isn't going the way you hoped."

- A picture of a dumpster fire. The dumpster is labeled "Strobe Witherspoon's America."

- A picture of a sad Keanu Reeves sitting on a park bench looking down. Under the picture reads: "HOW PEOPLE FEEL AFTER READING A BOOK BY STROBE WITHERSPOON".

- A YOUNG MAN holding hands with his GIRLFRIEND while admiring the rear end of another FEMALE PASS-ERBY. Above the YOUNG MAN reads "Strobe". Above the FEMALE PASSERBY reads: "Treasonous lies". The caption above the GIRLFRIEND reads "American Values".

- A picture of a stick figure at a typewriter. Next to the picture reads: "This is Strobe. Strobe is trying to sterilize the masses with his illuminati lizard person propaganda. Don't be like Strobe."

# 14

# Gut Check Podcast

## with Jordan Jennison

### episode 1328: Strobe Witherspoon

---

Transcript

---

**SW:**  Is this on?

**JJ:**  You gotta put the cans on?

**SW:**  The what?

**JJ:**  Headphones. Industry slang.

**SW:**  Ah. How 'bout now? This on?

**JJ:**  Yeah. You good. You comfortable? You need anything?

**SW:**  You have tea?

**JJ:**  No.

**SW:**  Coffee?

**JJ:**  No.

**SW:**  Water?

**JJ:**  There's some bottles under your feet.

**SW:**  I don't see them.

**JJ:**  You don't?

**SW:**  Hold on

         [LOUD BANG]

**JJ:**  Was that your head?

**SW:**  Found the water.

**JJ:**  Nice. You good?

**SW:**  Yeah. Lemme adjust my underpants.

**JJ:**  [Laughing] Yeah man, you get comfy. Boxers?

**SW:**  Briefs.

**JJ:**  This is going great.

**SW:**  Lemme know when you wanna start.

**JJ:**  We started two minutes ago. This is the podcast. Just shootin' the shit.

**SW:**  Ah. Well. Hello. How's it going?

**JJ:**  You know. Just tryin' to numb the loud ringing in my ears.

**SW:**  You have tinnitus?

**JJ:**  I was referring to the piercing squeals of existential despair.

**SW:** Why haven't I done this show before?

**JJ:** I try to keep it loose. If this goes well, we're going to get a better sense for what makes you tick, how you got into this hot mess you're in now, you know. Gut check.

**SW:** I get it. Podcasts. [TAKES A DRINK OF WATER INTO MICROPHONE]

**JJ:** Sorry man, I sound like I'm talkin' to a 12-year-old about some new fad.

**SW:** It's OK. People think I'm this cranky ol' hermit that unleashes invective on my typewriter from a shed in the woods.

**JJ:** That's not true?

**SW:** Well, I don't use a typewriter. Anymore.

**JJ:** You living in the woods these days?

**SW:** I have a place I go to when I'm not in Boston. It had a typewriter in the beginning. Then I got a computer that can't connect to the internet. That's actually where I drew inspiration for my first novel. Where everyone abandons computers because they are spying on them. Everyone starts using typewriters. You remember that one?

**JJ:** I do not. I have a computer in my bedroom, a computer in my living room where I work on scripts and tweet and write angry emails to my managers. Then I'm on my phone. Everywhere. I'll just up and stop talking to people in the middle of a lunch meeting if I get an idea and start tapping away on this plastic brick that sits in my blazer pocket. It just calls out to me when I'm away from it. I get phantom vibrations. In my ribs. I'm sure I'm gonna miss an email from my agent who I secretly loath.

**SW:** You should alienate everyone you work with. That'll keep those pangs away.

**JJ:** But you haven't always alienated people. Not all of them at least. Some people still seem to be buyin' what you're sellin'.

**SW:** For now.

**JJ:** Right. Some people don't exactly love being on the other side of the Witherspoon blade I take it.

**SW:** Yeah. I used to write action thrillers. Then something happened. I started just letting loose on everybody, on society, on politicians, thinking that would be the end of me. But it wasn't. People started buyin' it. And then I started acting it in my day-to-day life. And more people seemed to like it. Now I'm just it. Hard to say which hand washes the other.

**JJ:** Maybe both hands are unclean.

**SW:** I don't get it.

**JJ:** I take it you don't make it to too many Hollywood parties.

**SW:** Try not to. I was out here for the release of my last book, then for a bunch of meetings about the film rights. I got dragged to one. Then, ah, I... have you ever been to a party where something happens in a bathroom and that's all anybody can talk about?

**JJ:** Like sex and drugs?

**SW:** No.

**JJ:** I don't...

**SW:** My stomach. Wasn't cooperating.

**JJ:** Ah.

**SW:** A lot of people didn't appreciate that.

**JJ:** Were you embarrassed? I probably would have had a nervous breakdown and gone home before even sitting down on that toilet in the first place.

**SW:** I get kind of defiant in those situations. My tendency is to really embrace it.

**JJ:** A lot of people got a sense of what you had for dinner?

**SW:** I made sure to go over it in detail. Like I stood there and basically did a standup set about it.

**JJ:** Did you kill?

**SW:** I bombed. Literally.

**JJ:** Boom.

**SW:** Then I basically went on a rant about how all the

people at that party traffic in toilet humor for a living but think they're above it in real life.

**Editor's Note:** This has been cut down for brevity and relevance.

**JJ:** ...we sit in corners at these parties and group with other members of our tribe that share our sympathies on this and we condemn those that we see as unable to smell the stink of it all. No pun intended. And the cycle continues.

**SW:** No matter how good the grass-fed gluten free Doritos are.

**JJ:** I picture you growing up eating lobster rolls on a windy pier, with a really thick sweater on and an exceptionally long scarf.

**SW:** Wasn't really our style.

**JJ:** What'd your father do for a living?

**SW:** Well, he worked for the State department for most of his career. Different postings. We were based out of Boston for a while but we spent a fair amount of time in DC and New York growing up. Lots of different schools. A couple of postings in North Africa – Tunisia, Egypt. But we kept the house in Maine. Then he retired early and taught at a community college. And sulked.

**JJ:** I wasn't close with my father. He's dead. Your dad and you?

**SW:** We were close when I was young. Then my older brother, Wheeler, died. He was the promising one. Olympic hopeful. The athlete that didn't blow up bathrooms at parties.

**JJ:** His death hit you hard?

**SW:** He was better than me at most things. He was into equestrian stuff. I used to help him around the stables and before competitions. Then... the accident.

**JJ:** Would it be wrong for me to assume your family isn't a grieving out in the open type.

**SW:** Not a lot of crying, no. A fair amount of passive aggressive blaming though.

**JJ:** Blaming?

**SW:** There were people that blamed me for it. My father being one of them. The accident was, to some, preventable.

**JJ:** To you?

**SW:** I've stopped having that conversation with myself.

**JJ:** You don't think about it anymore?

**SW:** I think about it every day. But I've stopped blaming myself. Accidents are a bitch. The death of a brother never leaves you. But it started to destroy me. So I sunk myself into my work.

**JJ:** Am I remembering this correctly that this "work" factors into your current predicament?

**SW:** To people with an Internet connection and some frustrated Jack Ryan fantasies it does.

**JJ:** What does that mean?

**SW:** It means that my past government work is apparently some kind of clue. Some suggestion that I have information coming from the deep state about some... I can't even explain it without losing my temper. It doesn't make sense. And every fiber of my being wants to reject it to anyone that's listening. The notion that my former career somehow affords me inside access to criminal government networks that may have plotted an assassination of a sitting US president. And that for some reason I would then write a fictional novel that revealed that information as clues to others...

**JJ:** Right.

**SW:** But that's what they want me to do. Freak out and deny, deny, deny. Then they say that I'm obviously hiding something.

**JJ:** We're all hiding something. You have any idea what my emails look like?

**SW:** I don't.

**JJ:** Scary stuff. I used to, ah, email directors and agents that spurned me. I was not nearly the sophisticated and subtle wordsmith I am now.

**SW:** You mean like complaints? To your enemies in the industry?

**JJ:** Complaints is putting it lightly.

**SW:** What would putting it heavily be like?

**JJ:** Really long email rants during some, ah, long nights that would bleed into the morning. Just me and my computer. And my dealer's beeper number. Long story short, we all have some things in our past that can reemerge.

**SW:** Sure. But that's different. These fourteen-dimensional conspiracy claims go back generations and are just absurd. You believe in that shit?

**JJ:** The deep state?

**SW:** Yeah

**JJ:** I used to believe in it. But back then it was the hippies that were getting shook down by the feds. Now it's these militia bros and internet tough guys attacking the feds. But it's not that often I have someone on here that actually saw that government machinery first hand. You keep in touch with anybody from that part of your life?

**SW:** No. I didn't have any friends there. I sat at a desk. I wrote papers.

**JJ:** About what?

**SW:** Doesn't matter now. Nobody even read them.

**JJ:** But you drew from it in your next career as a writer. You mined it for professional gain.

**SW:** I just started making fun of it all. And maybe I contributed to this whole shitshow. Who knows? Making fun of the man seemed like a reasonable thing to do. Now there's millions of people making fun of everything and it all feels futile. But what else am I going to do?

**JJ:** You could write for television.

**SW:** You remember the TV show "Operation: Mindcrime"?

**JJ:** No.

**SW:** You remember the Queensryche album?

**JJ:** No.

**SW:** Well, I wrote on that show, loosely based on the 80's concept album of the same name. Went terribly. Then... you remember "Killing Me Softly"? About the seductive lady homicide detective with a potty mouth?

**JJ:** No.

**SW:** I created that show. Went terribly. The internet came after me and said "Strobe can't write women well."

**JJ:** I've heard that.

**SW:** It's a thing people say about me.

**JJ:** It's a thing.

**SW:** Well, I took it to heart!

**JJ:** How so?

**SW:** I wrote a book from a female perspective!

**JJ:** The new one? The FLOTUS book.

**SW:** Yes.

**JJ:** Is it done?

**SW:** Still tweaking a few sections that're either too on the nose or too esoteric or too pretentious. But I'm committed to cracking that code. Why? Because I'm an insecure idiot probably. Those criticisms got to me. All of the sudden I'm part of some larger war of agendas about that.

**JJ:** What about your agenda?

**SW:** You mean my agenda to mock people with agendas? That's my only agenda!

**JJ:** Is it?

**SW:** You think I got something else?

**JJ:** I think you want to get your point across.

**SW:** My point is that WE ARE ALL IDIOTS.

**JJ:** That's a good point. Feels like a good place to stop. How do you feel? You think this went well?

**SW:** No.

**JJ:** Seriously?

**SW:** I dunno. Coulda been funnier. Can I take the cans off now?

# 15

# Strobe Witherspoon is Us

## By Ned Stalworth

---

SPELUNKER - shining a light on our
dark, damp, despicable politics

---

UUUUUGGGGGGGGHHHHHHHH. Recently I made a deal
with myself that I would stop typing the words "I thought it
couldn't get any stupider" or any variation thereof, because
the functional reality of our world today is that "IT CAN
ALWAYS GET STUPIDER."

Which is to say that Strobe Witherspoon is fast becoming a
referendum on the viability of this website. He is revealing
the limits of our efforts to expose both the absurdity of our
current political predicament and the inhumanity of an internet fueled by the destructive forces of late Crapitalism™.

Strobe is us.

There seems to be a point where any take is an inherently
bad take. This story has reached that point. Because the
act of "taking" has become so competitively simplistic and

attention-seeking that, no matter how good our intentions, any effort to remedy the bad takes with a hot take simply creates an additional layer of bad take for others to take on top of. The resulting thousand layer take cake is so toxic to consume yet so irresistible that we are gonna need a crane to lift us out of this dark, damp cave of despair called America.

So, all you prospective hot takers out there, please think before you take. Maybe try and remember the plight of the Uighurs in Western China a little more and worry less about whether Strobe Witherspoon should write a novel about the former first lady. We at *Spelunker* are going to do that and we invite you all to do your best as well. Please, no more Strobe Witherspoon coverage. Seriously. Stop.

# 16

# The Curmudgeon's Dilemma

## By Jill Kowalczyk

The New Yorker

**B**ack in high school, I had what the Germans call *backpfei-fengesicht*, otherwise known as 'a face in search of a fist,'" Strobe Witherspoon tells me as we sit in the back of a Dunkin' (formerly Dunkin' Donuts) in Somerville, Massachusetts. This sounds like either a self-effacing way to say that other boys were preemptively putting him in his place—he was the perpetual new kid, son of a father who frequently moved for work—or an admission of being a young man whose disdain for others was difficult to conceal. Maybe it's both; that seems to be a common conclusion when dealing with Witherspoon's oft-told quips about his childhood.

Witherspoon is nothing if not contradictory. The foreign policy analyst, turned novelist, turned meme punching bag would like the readers of this profile to know that he is just an approachable doofus who likes to tell silly stories. Those stories, he will also tell you, just happen to be deeply distraught meditations on the human condition. His most recent novel, *FLOTUS: A Memoir*, continues this tradition.

*FLOTUS* set off a bidding war in the publishing industry and elevated Witherspoon's profile to levels he seems to embrace, mock, and fear in equal turns. A lack of detail about *FLOTUS* mixed with increased attention to Witherspoon's background has only served to fan the flames of internet speculation. The results of this spike in all things Witherspoon are, by now, not surprising: threats to his physical well-being, calls for his arrest, and skyrocketing commercial demand for his writing. In learning more of Witherspoon's story, I was hopeful that I could clear up some of the conjecture and inject a modicum of civility into this "Online Outrage Fiesta"—or OOF, in internet parlance.

Witherspoon himself does not always adhere to the rules of civility. He revels in his radical provocateur reputation, frequently augmenting it with his now-familiar caustic self-deprecation: "Don't these people have anything better to do with their time than let some WASPy has-been ruffle their feathers? Can't they just let me tell my stupid stories in peace?"

*FLOTUS*, as Witherspoon tells it, is "Just a fun story about a female immigrant who woke up one day as the wife of the President, told from her perspective." Just as soon as he finishes that sentence, he transitions to loftier, more contradictory territory: "Not for nothing, it also dives headfirst into the festering wound of politics and identity in today's America."

Some wonder whether this is a perspective Witherspoon should be presenting. On the right and left, there are questions about Witherspoon's political posturing. There have been complaints, particularly from the former President's supporters, that Witherspoon is making light of a very dark time in recent American history, a time that does not lend itself to irreverent satire. But that also seems like the exact reason an author like Witherspoon would broach such an issue. Striking when the fire is hot is a critical component of any radical provocateur's brand strategy.

For the former FLOTUS's critics, Witherspoon's efforts to casually humanize and normalize a profoundly polarizing figure—all while mocking that person's immigrant experience—inspires similar rage.

Witherspoon won't divulge much more about *FLOTUS*. At a book event in Cambridge, Massachusetts, right as the *FLOTUS* criticism was starting to percolate, he told an interviewer: "I would prefer to let the book speak for itself," before leaning back and surveying the crowd. His exasperated, unshaven smirk took on a more contemplative form. "I will say that I think it's going to, I hope, show a side of my writing, my humanity, that people haven't seen before." The same smirk makes appearances throughout the three weeks I spend with him in the greater Boston area, researching this piece.

"This is just a satirical take on the overwrought memoir craze," he tells me, "a criticism of the caricaturization of a person that few people really know, who just happens to be a female immigrant. I think I'm more than entitled to write about these things."

Witherspoon looked at me and took a sip of his coffee. "I don't like to shill for brands, but I make an exception for Dunkies," he said. "I bet you turn your nose up to this stuff."

"I only drink Polish tea," I said.

"Is this something I'm going to need to look into? Have the kids moved on from chai pumpkin frappilattes? Do I need to brush up on my Polish jokes?"

"It's what my parents drank."

When I explained to him that I'm a first-generation Polish immigrant and the only woman in my family to go to college, he dug his New Balance sneaker into the sticky Dunkin' floor. Maybe he sensed that the awkward eighth grader in me—the one with limited English skills, who was still thirty years away from winning a Pulitzer—had some opinions about his Polish joke references. Back then I had no clue why my classmates were all delighting in those jokes at my expense. I sometimes wonder if that experience led me to my current line of work. It also made me wonder about Witherspoon. Was he the ostracizer, the ostracized, or both?

Strobe Witherspoon, divorced with an estranged 23-year-old son, takes up a lot of space. His tall frame and propensity for gesticulation are easy to spot in a crowd. Facial expressions reminiscent of a mischievous high schooler are betrayed by his downtrodden eyes and gravelly voice, a testament to his years of unapologetic tobacco consumption.

He has an educational and professional pedigree any mother would be proud of. And his mother is proud. "Strobe always was the smartest, best son a mother could have, even when he was an obnoxious clown," Ruby Witherspoon said. His résumé backs her up: Andover to Swarthmore to the CIA. But Witherspoon mostly refers to his upbringing and education as an era when the seeds of his discontent grew into a thorn bush of malice against New England elites.

This anti-elitist disposition seems to endear Witherspoon to the Dunkin' patrons. "Wat's good, you faakin' faakface?" a young man in a throwback Gronkowski Patriots jersey and cargo pants yells at him when he enters.

"Language! I've got company, dipsh-t. She's from New Yaaawk!" Witherspoon yells as another patron sits down with us, uninvited. This time, it's an older gentleman with a strong limp and rosy cheeks. A ribald exchange about Irish people and alcoholism ensued, most of which can't be repeated in this publication.

The patrons of this particular Dunkin' rarely call it that, typically preferring its original moniker or "Double Ds" or "Dunkies" or "Dunky Doodle Dandy." And they all appear to revere Witherspoon. Our conversation is interrupted numerous times. I begin to sense that Strobe has orchestrated this. "They don't know you," he says. "They wanna make sure you're on the level."

People we met seemed almost disappointed if Strobe didn't make fun of them. This phenomenon was not limited to working-class Irish men on the outskirts of Boston. "Nobody knows why he can get away with it," his New York agent, Dan Manson, told me at his book signing in Cambridge. "He'll just lay into people about how much he hates everything about Cambridge, including the people, Harvard, bookstores, books—and these rich nerds will just chortle and golf clap away. I call him 'the WASPy Don Rickles.'

"In all honesty, I think people appreciate his approach these days more than ever. He's a wise-ass's wise-ass," Manson said. "And with all the real vitriol going around, and the tension about who can say what to whom, his ability to transcend that is what's really getting people to take notice of him in the industry. His early screenplays were serious affairs, with serious spies doing serious things. And that paid his bills for a little bit, but it wasn't him. Once he really loosened up and started peering into his cold, dead heart, that's when things started happening for him." Manson chuckled. "That's a Strobeism right there, using 'cold, dead heart' in an endearing way."

But many of his friends will tell you that when he lets his guard down, Witherspoon is a genuinely warm person. "I stopped drinking because of Strobe," an old classmate confides. "He was relentless and steadfast in his support for my sobriety. Never took a swig in front of me. Never talked down to me. Despite what he is gonna tell you, he's got a big heart."

A number of people I talked to use the phrase "big heart" to discuss their affection for Witherspoon. His agent, his former bosses, his teachers.

"Strobe is really just a big softy, such a big heart," Amber Witherspoon told me over coffee at Café Zing in Cambridge. "He is the reason my business is booming."

Amber is Strobe's cousin and the CEO of bookjacketquotes.com, a service that helps authors solicit and write quotes that can be used for book publicity. They maintain exclusive arrangements with a number of highly sought-after personalities in the industry.

"He put a lot of publishing companies in touch with me over the years. You know how important book jacket blurbs are for them, right?"

Amber waited for me to nod affirmatively.

"We have exclusive relationships with some of the best writers out there. When they need blurbs or quotes for their books, they come to us. And when we need something from them for another book ... boom, synergy."

When asked about claims that her business operates like a book-jacket mafia scheme where Strobe was the crime boss— a quid pro quo of endorsements from authors who feel compelled to provide them so they will get the best endorsements for their books, Amber demurred.

"We streamline the process. That's it. Creative disruption is gonna ruffle a few feathers, I get it, Cousin Strobe gets it," Amber said, and rattled off all of the high-profile clients she has. "You seem like you might have a book in you," she told me. "If you ever get around to writing it, lemme know; we can work something out."

Some have speculated that Amber's behind-the-scenes work for Witherspoon is fanning the flames of outrage and helping to raise his profile and her business. She denies such allegations over email, but not without the well-worn caveat that "#anypublicityisgoodpublicity."

"I love that he is doing so well with his writing," a former teacher at Andover, and now a friend of Witherspoon's, told me. "Sure, he was a little disruptive sometimes, as many high-energy high school boys are, but he wasn't disruptive in the ways that the 'bad kids' were. His jokes were at least about the material. And sometimes they were well observed."

During our time together, Witherspoon responded to questions about his education and his former profession with coy suggestions of mischief and disdain but few hard facts. His obfuscation and self-deprecation afforded him an air of mystery that he relished. As I talked to other friends and colleagues about him, details were also scant and vague. And yes, like Witherspoon, they were contradictory.

Was he a good student? Popular? A slacker? A bully? A deep-cover intelligence agent with access to highly classified information or just an entry-level CIA desk jockey? Even the people who know the answers seemed to be unwilling to divulge them. Or if they did give answers, they were demonstrably false.

"Somehow, he would show up for the SATs and ace them. Same with finals and other big tests. He was not good at doing homework or reading or getting along with the popular kids," his former Andover teacher recalled.

"I was a mediocre student who somehow did well enough on tests to get into good schools," Witherspoon told me.

None of that was true.

His SAT scores were mediocre. His grades were good. He was in the honor society. He played varsity football, basketball, and baseball. His girlfriend was homecoming queen. All of these things were easily confirmed by yearbooks and transcript requests.

It's not uncommon for subjects of magazine profiles to try to sculpt a narrative about their pasts that conforms to a larger origin story and mythology of their choice. Sometimes, these narratives go unchallenged because of lack of information, access, or time to research their claims. But now that interest in these details has increased, so too has the scrutiny into the past of this man of many contradictions.

This attention does not do Witherspoon's narrative many favors. The more I dug, the more Witherspoon's slightly disingenuous sculpting exercise morphed into a decades-long charade that had little basis in reality.

Witherspoon talks about moving around a lot as a kid and always feeling isolated and depressed in his new schools, where the kids were mean to him. He blamed his alcoholic father for these circumstances. This alienation provided the foundational bricks of the wall of isolation that he would later mine in his misanthropic fiction and skepticism-laced nonfiction. That's the story.

Except it's not entirely clear that the family moved around all that much. Or that his father worked for the State Department. Available records do show that the family had an address in Furstable Manor, in northern Maine, that they mostly used during the summer. They had an address in Brookton, Massachusetts, a relatively affluent suburb of Boston. School records show that Strobe went to public school in Furstable Manor until first grade and a public school in Brookton for second to ninth grades. He entered Andover in the tenth grade and stayed there until graduation. Not exactly a static childhood, but far from the nomadic lifestyle of a son of a US diplomat and the "new school every year or two" that he frequently references.

This discrepancy was in the realm of moderate overstatement, but when it came to his father's career, things got murkier.

Brookton Community College confirmed that Richard Witherspoon was an English as a second language (ESL) teacher there during much of Strobe's childhood. Not all of it, but more than Strobe would have you believe.

Was Strobe manufacturing a false origin story in order to appear more mysterious and interesting? All of this should be easy to confirm with Richard Witherspoon. But when I did track him down at his studio apartment in Maine (in a town he asked me to not identify), his disdain for his son's writing career was all he would discuss. "Look, I'm not talking about the past—where we lived, what we did. What I did. All that info is out there if you know where to look. What you should know is that I have no living sons. None. Both are dead. Wheeler died in an accident twenty years ago. And Strobe is dead in my eyes because of the crap that he calls writing. I didn't raise him like that. Someone got to him. Brainwashed him. I dunno. And I refuse to … that's it." Richard, whose friends call him "Tricky," trailed off. "Now, if you'll excuse me, I'm gonna go back inside." Richard closed his door and left me standing on the outside walkway of a building complex that was notably less posh than Witherspoon folklore would suggest.

Some would take Richard's reticence to speak to me as evidence of a life not intended for unclassified consumption.

Strobe's "State Department" references are a dead giveaway, a coy suggestion that Richard's career was spent somewhere within the US government apparatus that preferred not to advertise the identities of its employees—sometimes installing them in diplomatic positions as covers, other times in nondescript positions at community colleges—where their research was a front for some other nefarious intelligence-collection activity.

"He won't tell you what he was really up to, so I wouldn't even talk to him," Witherspoon told me when asked about his father. "And I don't know. We were very young when we were in North Africa; it's all kind of a blur. And then he started traveling more for work without the family. When he did come around, he would apologize for not being able to talk about it. That was a long time ago, though. Before the accident."

His brother's accident, and the ensuing guilt about it, is something Witherspoon alluded to frequently. So then why did Wheeler's obituary and death notice list the cause of death as "natural causes"? Twenty-four-year-olds don't normally die from "natural causes."

"We were a private family," Witherspoon said. "They wanted to call it natural causes; we didn't dispute it. He died at the hospital a few days after getting thrown from a horse on a saddle that was defective. I was the one who set up the saddle. I should've inspected it further. I didn't. I feel great shame for that. I will never not feel great shame for it."

As he told me this over a cigarette outside Dunkin', he waved off an acquaintance who wanted to chat. "After Wheeler's death, my relationship with my father deteriorated," he said. "No matter what I did, he blamed me for his favorite son's death."

Even here, the favorite son story starts to get confusing.

Wheeler was not nearly as good a student as Strobe, according to available records. He was not the son who went into his father's business. In fact, equestrian sports of any kind seemed to offend Richard Witherspoon's masculinity. I asked Richard about it while he closed the door on me. "That was his mother's thing. I was never into that floofy horsey crap. Not a sport. Good-bye."

When I pressed Witherspoon on some of these confusing details from his father, he bristled. "These types of matters aren't for public consumption. My family didn't ask for this. I may have chosen this godforsaken career in the public eye, but my father chose the opposite—to live in the shadows. I have to respect that, regardless of what he thinks and says about me these days." Witherspoon lit a Marlboro Red with the last match he had.

Even in deflection, Witherspoon seemed to all but admit that his father was working clandestinely for the US government. When asked why he doesn't just clear all of this up, Witherspoon paused. "Do you really think people will stop if we release ... what? Some papers that show what we were both working on during our time with the US government? No way." He stomped on his cigarette butt and walked inside, where he was greeted with a riotous "STROOOOOOOBE!"

Other family members I spoke to were equally evasive. Ruby, Richard's wife, no longer speaks to her husband. Technically, they are still married, but she told me, "We are not the types that divorce."

She did not know where Richard lived and seemed unable to remember when she last spoke to him. Her dementia made it difficult to push her on these subjects, but others in her senior living facility seemed to be unaware of Ruby's recent Alzheimer's diagnosis.

"Strobe keeps me going. He comes over all the time. He doesn't forget my birthday. He brings me newspaper clippings. I read all of his books and articles the second they come out." Ruby fiddled with the sweater she was knitting.

"Richard and I still love each other, but we do it separately," she said. "That was true even back when Strobe was growing up."

I asked when the marriage separation occurred. Ruby became distant and evasive. "Who can remember these things?" she said, returning to her sweater.

These and other prevarications lent a sliver of credibility to the otherwise outlandish rumors at the forefront of the growing scandal that is *FLOTUS: A Memoir*. Maybe the family *was* hiding something?

The US Intelligence Community is not the easiest place to get information from, particularly for journalists in my position, and particularly when you have very little to go on. A search into real estate records was more fruitful. Records show that the houses in Brookton and Furstable Manor were solely owned by Ruby. This would not have been terribly peculiar, considering the shadowy circumstances of Richard's supposed career before the community college job. However, additional records of Richard's employment at the community college indicated that he had been working there since at least the time of Strobe Witherspoon's birth. There were also records of a Richard Witherspoon who lived a few towns over for most of that period of time.

Strobe's response, that this was probably a clerical error, was not exactly reassuring. "Do you know how many Richard Witherspoons there are in Mass and Maine?" he asked me.

There were four Richard Witherspoons during that time period in question. Two of them are dead and did not work or live anywhere near Boston or Maine. The other one lived in Boston and said he had never heard of the property when I contacted him.

I revisited Ruby to ask her about this Massachusetts apartment two towns away that Richard seemed to own for most of Strobe Witherspoon's high school, college, and early professional years.

"Oh, that apartment? I think he just went there to clear his head sometimes," she said.

"Why didn't he tell Strobe about it?" I asked.

Ruby's face closed up, and she stammered something about maybe misremembering and that she needed to lie down because the meds take a lot out of her.

What was once an amiable relationship between writer and subject started to grow chillier. Witherspoon began to not-so-subtly suggest that neither of his parents were mentally able to cooperate with this piece and that my continued questions were disrupting their quiet existences.

"Quiet" would not be a word that could be used to described Richard Witherspoon's online existence. His posts on Facebook come in at an average of ten per day. They are almost always political in nature and frequently apocalyptic in tone, and they trafficked in extreme positions of anger, certainty, and jingoism (things that Strobe Witherspoon's work openly mocks). These posts also betray an intense loneliness that is hard to miss.

> "I know no one is goin 2 take this seriously because the nexus of power even on these social networking sites is so damn focused on ignoring the glaringly obvious fact that we have lost control of our

country and our liberty at the hands of a cabal of
shadowy world government cranks such that these
types of pleas for people to wake up and smell the
odious sulfuric infofascism + suggestive manipulation making us all cogs in the growing charade
that is our country which is going to consistently
cede its primacy to those with their hands inside
our brains and their bootheels on our throats. History is IMPORTANTT. Does anybody hear me?"

Richard's posts were typically accompanied by news stories
from "alternative news" websites about the growing scourge
of central banks, globalists, and political correctness. This par-
ticular post from 2017 linked to a story entitled: "WHY THE
RECENT DECISION TO LET CHINA BUY OUR DEBT
IS A SMOKESCREEN AND WHAT WE ALL NEED TO
DO TO EXPOSE THIS PLOT AGAINST OUR ECO-
NOMIC SOVEREIGNTY."

Many times, I found his understanding of history to be
intriguingly esoteric, like when he pointed to Soviet-era cotton production policy in Uzbekistan and its role in bringing
down the republic, causing one of the largest and most under-
reported ecological disasters of the 20th century. "This is what
happens when governments don't respect the natural order
of man and their surroundings." After Googling "Uzbekistan
cotton farming," I agreed with him.

Untangling Richard Witherspoon's role in his son's career
was turning into a key missing plot point in Strobe's life that
had eluded me during my sit-downs with the author and the
people who know him. Their protection of him and his origin
story suggested there was a part of his life he preferred to keep
out of public view. Why he would want to do this remained
unclear. Was he embarrassed? Trying to protect his family?

Was his professional success tied to a story about someone he is not?

I drove up to Boston to see Witherspoon and try to mend fences.

He drank his coffee. I brought up his son, Mitch.

"His mother and I married young. When I left the agency and started writing, it put a big strain on us financially. Blah, blah, blah. I was a terrible father. He's better off without me. Don't ask me about his mother. She's off the grid. Off the grid, off the grid. I wish her the best. *That* you can put in your piece."

Mitch Witherspoon, however, is not difficult to find on the internet. He travels around the world, volunteering and exploring, documenting these activities via his vlog and blog, where he discusses the power of global citizenship and the spiritual rewards of touching the lives of the less fortunate.

"It's important that we tread lightly," he tells me. "I'm a guest in the places I travel to, that should be communicated clearly, gracefully." He is currently vlogging from a hostel in Amsterdam, but he wants his audience to know that he is about to go to India.

Like Richard Witherspoon, Mitch's online persona is strikingly different from Strobe's. Exploring Mitch's seemingly bustling business—the views on his YouTube videos occasionally reach the millions—can be disorienting. His approach mixes selfless altruism with relentless self-promotion, as explained in the "About" section of his website: "my goals are twofold: engage and support local communities while inspiring my digital brothers and sisters to do the same."

"I don't think it takes that much to realize that my father and I are different people, ya know? I used to be a little more angry about it. We had some showdowns when I was younger. Now, I'm about showing gratitude and openness," he told me, putting his hands together into a prayer position and bowing his head to the computer camera.

"His brand is more about malice. And keeping secrets. Each his own. I get that he's angry about a lot of things," Mitch said as he tucked his long wispy brown hair behind his ears.

Even though he was in a bustling café, rife with marijuana smoke and laptop-bound digital nomads from around the world typing furiously, Mitch seemed undistracted and happy to expound at length about his worldview; a comfort and eloquence gained from years of first-person pontification in hectic environments.

> Right now I'm in Amsterdam. So many bikes here to just ride around and explore. Who doesn't love bikes in cities? They connect us. Like the internet—also such an important connecter. A lifeline to the world and my followers—I mean fans, I mean peers. My dad, he seems to be fighting technology, not embracing it the way I do. He also seems to be fighting the tide of change that is sweeping through society. He's always talkin' about the partisan divide and the great dumbing down of America but I'm just like, 'Let's not focus on the divide, focus on the connections.' And I get those all over the world.

I asked him to describe his childhood and his relationship with his father.

> After the divorce, my mom got real into home-schooling and keeping me out of harm's way. She was about love and spirituality. Which was cool. But she kept my internet time down to 30

minutes a day. That wasn't awesome. Ultimately, I was like, I need to see this world! She didn't take it real well. My parents are both kind of skeptical about the internet, and I embrace it. In that way, I'm rebelling against my upbringing. But also, my dad's a writer, and he likes to communicate with the world, and so do I. So we aren't that different! And my mom, she's into positivity and so am I. So I'm kinda just carving my own path, with their paths always a little bit in the frame—a little bit from this truth bucket; a little from that truth bucket. That's me. My dad—I get it—his child-hood, he didn't have that. You know, there were lies. I think that messed him up a little.

"What kind of lies?" I asked.

"Oh man, you know. His dad. Wasn't what he said he was. My dad dedicated his life to pleasing his dad. That was harsh."

I asked him to elaborate on the lies.

"He didn't tell you? Oh."

Mitch clammed up. He told me he had to get to his holis-tic capoeira training.

"Mitch has a real active imagination," Strobe told me.

"So you don't think your father was living a lie? Was he always just living a few towns away, but telling you that he was a secret agent? Not coming around for long stretches?"

"Is that what you think?" Witherspoon stared at me.

"I'm just trying to get a better understanding of your journey."

"I think you're tryin' to ambush me," Strobe said. "My dad's not the subject of this conversation. Details about his life are not for public consumption. For me, I'm very candid about the four years I spent at the agency after I graduated. I wasn't undercover. I was a researcher. I wrote papers. In Langley, Virginia. That's where I lived with my wife. We had a kid. Then I left the agency." Witherspoon got up from the table and began literally talking down to me in short, curt statements.

"I wrote a few screenplays about the CIA. They didn't sell. The family was broke. I took off like an immature brat. I moved back to Maine. Five years later, I sold my first CIA script. They turned it into a franchise. I started writing other scripts. Then I sold a book of short stories. Then a novel. Then some other stuff. A few scripts in between. And here we are today. Slumaahville, Mass. Drinkin' some Dunky Doodle Dandy. Anything else you need to know? No? Good luck with the rest of the piece."

Witherspoon exited the premises while reaching for his cigarettes. Emails and calls went unreturned after that. His ex-wife, Miranda, declined to be interviewed for this piece.

Fellow novelist Horace Witherspoon (brother to Richard, father to Amber, uncle to Strobe), seemed like the last Witherspoon willing to talk when I reached out to him. His career has not been met with the same critical and commercial success as his nephew's, but Strobe points to him as an inspiration and a source of guidance in his early years. He said he was particularly indebted to Horace's first novel, *Are There Chicken Nuggets in Heaven?*

Just before our scheduled call, Horace sent me an email:

> My nephew is an extraordinary talent with a big heart. His perspective on the decline of the American experiment is a unique and important one. Any salacious speculation about his previous line of work, or that of his father (my brother), is nonsense, pure and simple. It is an attempt to

squash Strobe's important voice by the lunatic
fringe. Because of the hyper-reactionary world
we inhabit, where everybody is yelling at the top
of their lungs about issues they know little about,
I fear that any additional attention paid to this
matter will only make things worse. For that reason, I have opted to limit my participation in your
project to this statement. Thank you in advance
for respecting my wishes on this topic.

Warm Regards,
Horace Witherspoon
Acclaimed author of *Ice Skating in Somalia*

In the early days of this assignment, I found most of the
claims against Strobe Witherspoon to be nothing short of
preposterous—a sad reminder of an ignorant and overzeal-
ous online community eager to destroy a man's credibility in
order to reinforce its existing belief system. I still feel that way.
Sort of.

On the subject of *FLOTUS: A Memoir*, not much has
been revealed that wasn't already in the public domain. And
I am neither legal expert nor literature critic, and therefore
find myself ill-equipped to expound upon any deeper decon-
struction of the internet's heated response to this forthcoming novel.

My task was to learn more about the man behind the novel.
On that front, progress was made. Incomplete progress, but
progress nonetheless.

The circumstances of Strobe's upbringing were fraught. His
relationship with his father—or lack thereof—likely loomed
large over his life choices and his work: the once strait-laced
scholar/athlete who dated a homecoming queen and went to

the best schools chose to reject that life in his mid-20s, seemingly without warning. He turned his back on a career at the Central Intelligence Agency, and on a young wife, a child, and the father that he'd once looked up to. Now, he appears driven to muzzle and deflect any and all efforts to uncover this biographical information.

It seems reasonable to deduce that the father Strobe thought he knew turned out to be something different. Was this disappointing demise of his once-role model the "Rosebud" of this story? Perhaps. The driving force behind Strobe's commitment to his radical provocateur image? Unclear.

There seems little doubt, however, that Witherspoon has taken great pains to create and promote a certain narrative about his life that is not entirely accurate. But why, and by how much does it deviate from the truth? Is this deviation an at-the-margins fudging? Or is it a whole-cloth reinvention that requires constant maintenance and subterfuge from a tight-knit network of inner-circle enablers? And what to make of the death of his brother, Wheeler? How much does Ruby Witherspoon remember or factor into these stories? For these questions, there seem to be, as yet, no easy answers.

Just prior to going to press with this article, I received an email from Strobe's agent, Dan Manson. The subject header read, "On Behalf of Strobe Witherspoon," and within the body of the message was a statement from Witherspoon:

> For the majority of my writing career, I have spoken publicly about the challenges that beset myself and my family growing up in New England—particularly the difficult events around my brother's death and my estrangement from my father. Those experiences have had lasting effects on my

work and my family. On occasion, these traumas
have resulted in delusional episodes. During these
episodes, I have sometimes misrepresented certain components of my family history. Some of
this misrepresentation included the implication
that my father was in some way employed by the
US Government intelligence community. Ther-
apy has revealed to me that these misrepresenta-
tions are likely linked to my longstanding struggle
to reconcile my role in my brother's death and
the impact this had on my family. I constructed
these stories to deflect and distract. In hindsight,
I am deeply sorry for any confusion or misunderstanding that these delusional episodes may have
caused. It was not my intention to mislead or create any type of mystery around my upbringing for
the sake of my career—it was simply my brain's
way of distorting certain events to dilute their
crippling impact on my mental health.

If Tolstoy is right that "All we can know is that we know nothing. And that's the height of human wisdom," then I may now
be a certified genius. Witherspoon's uncharacteristic act of openness and contrition has only served to solidify my confusion.

The Witherspoonian contradictions in his statement
abound. On the one hand, he appears to be showing the
strains of a decades-long storyline that has gotten away from
him and may threaten the brand he has sought to shape to his
liking. On the other, buzz surrounding Witherspoon's forthcoming book and its intersection with his at least partially false
brand means that there has never been a better time to be in
the Witherspoon business. Mysterious author biographies can
be particularly good for business.

At the time of this writing, Google Trends continues to show a noticeable uptick in all search activity related to Strobe Witherspoon. His publishing company is doubling down on its commitment to this property and publicly fighting back. To me, the company reiterated its position: "Our support for Witherspoon remains firm. Efforts to bully us via boycott threats and cyber-attacks will only strengthen our commitment to this work, the publishing industry, and the unparalleled importance of the written word in the increasingly crowded marketplace of ideas."

However, boycott efforts are becoming increasingly effective tools in our outrage-fueled idea marketplace. And while the veracity of the most outlandish claims against Witherspoon continue to suffer from a credibility deficit, the ambiguity surrounding his background makes it likely that this outrage fiesta has not yet reached its nadir. Hopefully, the lights will come up on this fiesta via an honest and open appraisal of the facts. But if past is precedent, that may be wishful thinking.

# 17

# RITATWEETZ1999

Tweet Storm

1/ finished tedious @thenewyorker article about the literary Vanilla Ice. SOOOOOO LOOOOOOONGGGG. Was the editor on vacation?

2/ Guess what? I hav thoughts. SPLR ALRT: the call is coming from inside the house. And it's full of sanctimonious centrists with no spine. Settle in.

3/ Why is nobody pushing him on that top secret illuminati job? Im gonna say it. Everything that dude says is sketchy. He was a CIA AGENT!!!! #QUESTIONAUTHORITY

4/ The #misogyny is too much. Strobe does not respect the Polish author. Isn't interested in her opinion. Obviously giving her the @strobewither he wants the world to see.

5/ the journo meekly hinted at her Polish immigrant background, then DID ABSO FUKN LUTELY NUTHN to check his priv about it.

6/ This is why we can't trust the Mainstream left.

7/ I cant sit back and let this slide @thenewyorker. Do better than that.

8/ After I finish this tweet, put in my shift at the campus cafeteria study til the library kicks me out I'm going 2 go check on mi madre's dialysis.

9/ Whats ur sched look like Strobe? I didn't think so.

10/ Boycott.

11/ End Rant.

# 18

**Editor's Note:** *This email is reprinted here with permission from Ruby Witherspoon. It was sent to Strobe from his mother while the* New Yorker *profile was being written. It is chronologically out of order in this compendium in that it corresponds with the moment Strobe stopped cooperating with Jill Kowalczyk, the journalist writing the piece.*

**From: Ruby Witherspoon ‹ruby.witherspoon@aol.com›**
**To: Strobe Witherspoon ‹swither@wthrspnllc.com›**
**Subject: Hello**

Dearest Strobe,

I hope this note finds my Strobelight well.

I had Leslie at the computer center set this up. I was going to send it to you in handwritten form, which is how I wrote it, but I remembered that you told me you don't open your mail anymore because it's all bleeping bull bleep.

I know that these are difficult times for our family. I suspect you are feeling the difficulty in a particularly acute way. With all of this new attention on your work, it may surprise you to learn that I too have been forced to confront certain things about our past.

A reporter came over to talk to me. I was originally comfortable with her questions. I felt like she was going to represent you and us well in her article and perhaps a feature in *The New Yorker* could help you offset some of this negative attention you are receiving. Also, I deeply admire that publication, and I was so proud and excited for you to be featured in it. I told others at the center, and many of them were very impressed.

But then this woman began asking questions about Richard. I didn't say anything too revealing, but I fear that her investigations will be no match for my half-hearted senility act and the decades of deflection and suppression that our family has been engaged in.

Which brings me to the main purpose of this letter. Maybe you can talk to the reporter and correct some things you may have said in error. Before the article comes out.

I have been bearing the weight of a lot of bad decisions made around the time of your birth and extending to, well, about the time when you and your father had your falling out. That's almost a quarter of a century of weight on my arthritic shoulders. Ouch.

Here goes.

Your father was not who he said he was. He was an alcoholic (which you probably already know). He also had a temper (which you only occasionally witnessed). The reason he was able to keep the severity of his problem from you was that he was not around a lot. But not for the reasons you think. He frequently went on long "trips" to feed his addiction and avoid his own failings—as a father; as a baseball player who never made it. Who knows what else. But none of those trips were "top secret."

You ate it all up. Looking back on the truth, it's unconscionable that I would do such a thing to someone I loved—to you.

Your father and I fell out of love soon after you and your brother were born. If I'm being completely honest, I fell out of love with your father, and I don't really know if he was ever in love with me.

By the time you were eleven, I told him I couldn't do it anymore. The verbal abuse. The physical abuse. The raids on my (read: my parents') bank account for the "top secret" missions. I couldn't bankroll his reckless, useless lifestyle anymore, so I told him to get out. And I sent you off to that expensive boarding school to shield you. And to shield me from your disappointment.

When you were younger and your father and I were still living together, the CIA stories seemed harmless. I think they made him feel strong. Stronger than real life, where he was never the breadwinner. I felt like I should let him have that fleeting sense of strength and authority that he felt when he was dropping hints about his exciting, albeit fake, life. I thought I owed it to him, at first because of my own preconceived notions of a man and woman's role in bringing up their children. Later, I thought I owed it to him for upending those roles when I kicked him out. I was wrong both times. I owed him nothing.

When he was employed, he was an ESL community college teacher—that much is true. The stories he told to hide that fact were manipulative and disgraceful. Watching you take it all in with such excitement was torture for me. Watching you base your career choices on those stories was even worse.

By the time you went to college and started working at that job in Virginia, your father and I hadn't been together for many years. His growing absence in your life wasn't because his work was getting more dangerous, taking him out of the country for long stretches or to secret meetings in Tunisia, or New York or Washington, DC. It was because he was an alcoholic who lived two towns away and didn't come over. When he used to say, "Sorry, kid; if I told you what I'm workin' on, I would have to kill you," I must confess to wishing it was he who was dead.

But none of this compares to our family's biggest lie. You know what I'm talking about. I could always see it in your face. I could see that you wanted me to fix it. And I didn't. For that, I will never forgive myself.

All I can hope for is some level of absolution—from our holy savior, and from the son who is all that I have left in this material world that I am probably not long for.

I hope you can forgive me. And I hope to see you soon.

Always,
Ruby

# 19

# Liberty Lisa's Victory Vlog #287

Transcript

**LL:**  I have two words for you.

BOY.

COTT.

Our liberty is not for sale. The big news agencies all have relationships with the big publishing companies. Who work with the big spy agencies. Like the one Strobe Witherspoon worked for out of college. You heard him admit it!

Over at the hoity toity New Yorker we were graced with an in depth look into Strobetard's treasonous deception.

Sounds like someone's been telling more fibs than a "Climate" scientist.

My question to you, esteemed followers of mine, is, 'what are you going to do about it?'

For my exclusive executive suite subscribers, I'm gonna sweeten the deal. Sign the petition on my home page, tweet at VITAL books that you are not going to buy any of their titles ever again if they publish this FLOTUS garbage, and tell all your friends to do the same. Send me evidence of your work and I'll give you 15% off my bobblehead doll and 20% off my branded mousepad. Ten randomly selected signers will get a free copy of my e-book—*Let's Take the Lib out of Liberty!* Available now on Amazon via my own imprint Truth Bomb Books.

# VITAL BOOKS

Statement

In recent weeks, we have been saddened by the baseless accusations and unwarranted attacks on Strobe Witherspoon and his forthcoming book from VITAL, *FLOTUS: A Memoir*. While we remain steadfast in our support for Mr. Witherspoon and refuse to be bullied into business decisions we do not agree with, we are also conscious of the growing risk to Mr. Witherspoon and his family surrounding the release of this book. For that reason, we are going to monitor this situation, and we kindly request your patience and respect for Mr. Witherspoon and his family's privacy as we continue to explore the best possible resolution.

**Editor's Note:** *Twitter had opinions.*

DAMN SON YOUR PUBLISHING COMPANY ABOUT
TO DROP YO ASS!!!! 🙂 🙁 !!!!!!

If this boycott succeeds in suppressing this author's
voice, we all lose

OUR VOICE MATTERS!!!!!!! Tell Strobe Witherspoon
to stop with his lies and his illuminati conspiracies
#boycottVITAL

THERE 🖐 IS 🖐 NOTHING 🖐 TO 🖐 BOYCOTT 🖐 THE 🖐
BOOK 🖐 HASN'T 🖐 EVEN 🖐 BEEN 🖐 RELEASED 🖐
YET

# Chapter 3:
# One Immigrant's Journey

---

FLOTUS: A Memoir
(draft: not for distribution)

---

In high school, my classmates were very unfriendly toward me. That level of hostility felt sadly familiar twenty years later, when I scrolled through exhortations on the internet: "your too fat for him," "suck your farts," "I hope you choke on his STD infested weener."

I had big plans, and these people could sense it, and that made them uncomfortable. Could I have maybe been a little less ostentatious? I guess I could have. My parents owned a successful chain of internet cafés (remember internet cafés?) and that gave me a level of access to the outside world that I relished. I spent my days after school helping my parents. And by helping, I mean surfing the internet. I followed all the celebrity news sites. Most of my classmates didn't have access to that kind of information. It set me apart.

When I started modeling, things only got worse. There were the girls and the terrible looks they gave me when I walked down the hall in the plaid miniskirt from the hit movie

*Clueless*. Then there were the boys and their gaping-mouthed stares. I acted like I was too good for them, because deep down I believed that I was.

Looking back, I sometimes think about what would have happened had I been more conservative in my dress and attitude. Perhaps I wouldn't have been recruited from that mall. Perhaps I wouldn't have landed that gig in New York. Perhaps I wouldn't have overstayed my visa. Perhaps I never would have met *him*. I think about that a lot.

But would I have been able to stay in Slovakia with that fire burning inside of me? I don't know. I had a lot of curiosity. Back in the day, I would race over to our largest café on Štefánikova Street. I would sit down at the desk, check in customers, and surf the web. When I was interrupted by someone who wanted to pay, I would involuntarily shoot them an angry stare. Didn't they understand that I was doing important research? I was learning about fashion, about runways, about photography.

Also, time was running out! I was almost done with high school. Soon, I would be aging out of the young waif modeling and runway jobs that I wanted much more than some mail-catalog pants-suit job that I thought was for women in their twenties.

But the spark that started this unfathomable journey came from an unlikely place: my sister Petra. She was better in school than me. She played by the rules. She was pretty in that tall, shy, brown-haired way Slovakian girls can be pretty. I always told her she should dye her hair blonde like me, and she always just shrugged.

"The boys prefer blondes!" I said. She wasn't interested.

Petra was committed to her medical studies and was dating a nice boy who was also going to be a doctor. She seemed happy for me, but I could tell that she was a little concerned about my path, my adventurous spirit.

And then she died.

All of the medical training in the world couldn't save her.

My father told me not to tell the police what I had seen. It wouldn't be good for the family, he told me.

They took me into a separate room. They had a lot of questions. I said I didn't see anything; didn't know anything about the railings.

Something inside of me died that day as well. I was no longer convinced that my heart was where my home was.

I felt trapped by the corruption—so many payoffs to so many government agents so they would "let" us continue running the internet cafes without harassment. I also felt trapped by my family. They were complicit in my sister's death. I knew I had to get out.

Dominik, my father, was grieving; I knew that. His favorite was gone, and negligence was the reason. He'd known that all of the balcony railings were old and needed replacing, but that would cost money that he didn't want to spend. A payoff to the inspectors—to avoid a citation—would be a fraction of the cost. So our family paid a different kind of penalty.

Now that my father is gone, I have decided I can no longer dishonor the memory of my sister. She deserves better. She didn't "fall" off of that balcony. Corruption, aided by my father's willingness to play by those rules, pushed her off that ledge. The things we do to save money.

Just as I owe it to Petra to honor her memory, I owe it to myself to process the choices I have made and make peace with them. My therapist tells me that there is much work to be done.

But it's important to remember that in Bratislava back in

those days you looked out for yourself and your loved ones, sometimes in ways that were necessary but uncomfortable. So, when it was time to get them American visas, I did it. I'm glad I did. I contributed to this great nation of immigrants, this melting pot of big dreamers with a lot to offer.

My parents grew to love it here. Over time they saw that this country had rules, and that those rules helped everybody. They didn't have to pay off building inspectors when they opened their first Greek restaurant. They adhered to the rules because they knew there would be consequences if they didn't. All of their restaurants were better off for it; the customers were better off for it. This country was better off for it.

I still love my heritage and my people. But the energy in America is infectious. This country has so much to offer people like me, people with big dreams and wild hearts.

In America, it's not about who you know—and we knew a lot of people in Bratislava!—it's about prospering on your own terms. Not some government official's terms.

"Moving here saved my life," my father told me, years later, when he first started chemotherapy at a state-of-the-art private hospital in New York City. He had his own room, doctors on call at all hours of the night, and the best medicine money could buy. In Slovakia in the 1990s this money would have likely been put toward paying off hospital administrators to get to the front of the line at the public hospital; as rich as we were, we would not have been able to afford treatment abroad.

I had another eight years with my father because of the treatment he received in New York.

I'm saddened (sometimes sickened) by news stories about immigrants who don't have that same appreciation for the United States. We should condemn them. We should not let those who stand against the values of this great country undermine the hard work of people like me—a simple Slovakian woman who saw what she wanted, worked hard to achieve it, and reaped the rewards of that hard work. The American dream is not dead. I am living proof of that. And I am a proud immigrant on a proud journey.

# 23

# Can We Even Read Anymore?

**By Horace Witherspoon**

---

Horaceblog.com

---

As a young man growing up in western Maine, I was always finding excuses to go to the library. The library helped me discover new worlds. It kept me from my father's belt. It kept me from the deafening silence of my house, when he would come home from work and brood—first in the kitchen, then in the sitting room, and finally in his bed. Waking him up was the worst outcome, so silence ruled.

My brother Richard Jr. didn't have the library. They banned him after the rat-carcasses-in-the-card-catalog incident. I often think about that dumb prank. I was a part of it. But Richard never told anybody about my involvement, so I didn't get banned.

That was a long time ago. I don't know if Richard Jr.'s life would have gone differently if he hadn't been banned from our area of respite in that one-horse town with nary a movie theater in sight. Perhaps that's naïve. Perhaps Richard Sr.'s genes would have always won out. But maybe not. If things were different, maybe my brother would have been the one to write eight novels, three novellas, two short story collections, and narrate the oral history of crabs for Maine Public Television. Who knows?

But here we are. Someone told me the other day that that same library in Maine made the news because a cache of over one thousand hours of pornography was found on its computers. In the library!

Which gets me to the question I posed at the top of this blog post: Can we even read anymore?

I read the Strobe Witherspoon *New Yorker* article, and I observed the response to it. I would like to offer my opinion. I am not, however, attracted to the language of shock and sensationalism that is *de rigueur* in most online circles these days. But I will say this: the outrage about my family is poppycock!

Yes, have a laugh at my outdated phraseology. Maybe you would like to take that language and put it on top of a picture of an old person with reading spectacles and a cane wagging his finger at the camera. Then send it far and wide via text and email to others, letting them know that my anger is old-fashioned and should be mocked by people who don't know me. Or perhaps caption that meme picture with a "you mad bro?".

That is not reading. That is just modern-day schoolyard taunting. Do people understand that?

My family is not a carnival show. The accusations against my nephew are not simply false, they are demonstrably false, and they are being propagated by individuals who do not possess even an iota of the same credibility that he has, which he has earned over many years.

I was eager to express this perspective in the pages of the *New Yorker*, a magazine I have long admired and, admittedly, has never accepted any of my proposals. But Strobe contacted me while the *New Yorker* article was being written and advised me otherwise. So I withheld details.

Thus, this blog post was born.

Do people even know how to read the *FLOTUS* chapters that the *New Journal* so brazenly leaked to the public? Strobe's work is literary satire of the highest order that interrogates the power imbalances of our time and the extremes of human behavior driven by those imbalances. Your silly picture with some text on it? That's just a silly picture with some text on it that is used to make the picture creator feel better about themselves with minimal effort and insight.

And our family, while far from perfect, deserves privacy. To be sure, my brother Richard has not always been honest, and his demons sometimes have resulted in behavior unfitting of the Witherspoon name.

The years after Strobe's birth were particularly hard on my brother. My books were selling well, and his baseball career officially ended in an alcohol-related injury that he never talked about. But it loomed large over everything he did moving forward.

During Strobe's childhood, many months went by when we didn't know where Richard was. Ruby would call me with concern, and I would sometimes come over to spend time with Strobe and Wheeler. I eventually became something akin to a father figure to those boys. I don't want to brag, but my literary tutelage during those years was instrumental in shaping Strobe's work. (Wheeler wasn't much of a reader.) When Strobe was in ninth grade, I gave him my copy of the Harvard Lampoon's *Bored of The Rings*. He read it in two days. From there, I moved to the classics, taking my first-edition Jonathan Swift novels out of their protective cases and letting him read them at his leisure. To my surprise, he tore through them all, sometimes literally, returning them in condition that significantly undermined their value for collectors. But it was worth it, as I can see a strong tonal and structural through line from those works—particularly *A Tale of a Tub* and *Gulliver's Travels*—in Strobe's work.

Richard would eventually emerge from his benders, looking a little worse for the wear. It was difficult to witness, because deep down we knew there was a good person in there. But that person needed to reconcile his relationship with his father, me, my success, alcohol, and a world that did not give him the opportunities he felt he deserved. That reconciliation remains a work in progress.

That is what you should know that wasn't emphasized in the *New Yorker* profile. My brother Richard is not a crackpot; he is a human being who has been lost for many years and is still trying to find his way. That reading shouldn't be that radical.

Will we be able to read like that once more? I am optimistic, as I am wont to be. But it will take commitment. Who is with me?

# 24

# Okay, Fine, Let's All Gawk at This

---

Spelunker

---

Dear America,

You win. I know I implored us all to look away from the dumpster-diving inferno of despair that is the Strobe Witherspoon saga.

No one listened.

And for good reason. Things have changed!

So, let's recap, shall we?

Boycotts threatened. A new excerpt of the book magically appears. It was stupid. Some nonsense about a sibling's death that seemed to mirror Strobe's own struggles with his brother's demise.

The "leak" was also incompetently planted by Strobe's book publicist (and cousin) Amber Witherspoon. Amber got found out. She played dumb.

**Amber Witherspoon Statement:**

> Recently a hard drive of mine was stolen. That hard
> drive contained excerpts of *FLOTUS: A Memoir* by
> my client, Strobe Witherspoon. I am saddened by
> the relentless attacks on Strobe that this affront to
> my privacy and Strobe's intellectual property has
> generated. I am also saddened by the criticism that
> has been leveled at me and my company, bookjack-
> etquotes.com. At no time did I play any part in the
> release of this chapter excerpt. My company and my
> clients are too important to me to risk damaging my
> best-in-class reputation for book publicity and book
> jacket content, a reputation that stands as a testa-
> ment to my hard work and perseverance. I refuse to
> have anyone debase the incredible success I have
> had and the overwhelmingly high satisfaction rate
> I get from my clients. Please refrain from sharing
> Strobe Witherspoon's excerpt for his forthcoming
> novel *FLOTUS: A Memoir*. If you don't, expect a letter
> from our legal team.

Strobe stayed silent. VITAL Books reached out to Buzzzzzzzzz
(the site that leaked the chapter) with a cease-and-desist
letter of their own:

> VITAL Books claims ownership of work related to the
> forthcoming publication of *FLOTUS: a memoir* a novel
> written by Strobe Witherspoon. We hereby demand
> that you cease and desist from the publication of any
> and all work related to that unpublished work imme-
> diately. Failure to cease and desist will result in legal

action pursuant to said failure and the collection of all available damages and remedies owed to VITAL Books under the law.

Buzzzzzzzzz didn't blink. The clicks were too important. Media moguls need to pay off their summer homes. Writers need to pay off their crushing student debt.

Crapitalism™ continues to eat itself in front of our eyes (h/t Karl M).

And Strobe? He continued to stay silent.

The internet didn't care. Because it was too busy weighing in on the excerpt.

**Literary Twitter had critiques:**

> I sense in this excerpt a strained relationship between author and protagonist; the pedantry doesn't resonate with me; the manufactured tension feels contrived; the satire feels stale. Pass.

> The tropes of archetypal womanhood are on full display in this excerpt. I'm intrigued by this Slovakian immigrant's struggle. I wonder if Witherspoon will make good on this provocative tidbit and sustain this multi-dimensionality throughout the manuscript.

> Is this the second coming of Kurt Vonnegut? Said no one ever after reading this excerpt.

**Woke Twitter had anger:**

> Looking forward to a white male winning Best Direc-
> tor Oscar for this when it gets turned into a sterile
> Hollywood flop!

> Finally!!!!!!! someone took on the important task of
> representing the struggles of a Slovakian super-
> model and her sketchy ass parents as they game
> the immigration system for their own benefit. That
> fixes everything. #sarcasm

> Great, the normalization of feminism's worst enemy
> marches on, thanks to the outdated satirical styl-
> ings of some doooooooooosh named Strobe. Hard
> pass.

**Conspiracy Twitter had conspiracies:**

> This just proves what I've been sayin all along – this
> dude will do anything to distract us, even plop out
> some fake excerpt to keep us from talking about
> what's really going on, AKA the wholesale deep
> stateification of our government by the lamestream
> media

> Now can we stop pretending that this lamewad
> ISN'T sending signals to the former POTUS's next

assassins? So many obvious signals. WHEN WILL
WE WAKE UP TO THIS THREAT!

Strobe is writing about his dead brother! It's so
obvious! Follow the crumbs. Wheeler Witherspoon's
death is the thread that links all of the illuminati
back to the Witherspoons! Keep up America!

Speaking of the lamestream media, they continued to provide the most vanilla takes you could imagine:

- *Provocative Novel Continues to Intrigue and Enthrall*

- *With Boycott Calls Gaining Steam, Publishing
  Company Braces for the Worst*

- *Hundreds Gather Outside VITAL Books to Protest
  Witherspoon Novel*

- *Amber Witherspoon Is Most Recent Family Member
  Caught Up in Novel Scandal*

Summary: Nobody knows what is happening, some people
are afraid of the implications of the boycott for the publishing industry, and other people think Strobe hastily put that
excerpt together to convince people his book isn't interested
in the assassination of a former president.

And still, the plutocrats don't care about the proletariat and
the Uighur genocide marches on with nary a peep.

# 25

**Editor's Note:** *This email is Strobe's response to Ruby Witherspoon's email. Of course, many have already seen this letter because of the hack* :(

From: Strobe Witherspoon <swither@wthrspnllc.com>
To: Ruby Witherspoon <ruby.witherspoon@aol.com>
Subject: Re: Hello

Hi, Mom,

Man, what a week. Recent events have been made worse by the realization that this ridiculous situation has now wrapped its unseemly tentacles around you. That is the last thing I wanted.

Regarding your previous email, thank you for your candor. I know it wasn't easy for you to write that (and please thank Leslie at the computer center for me!).

What can I say? I was originally thinking that I would tell you that I have known all of this information about Pop for a while. I would tell you not to worry about that stuff, it is all water under the bridge at this point, your love is all that's important to me.

But that would have been a lie. I never figured it out. Any of it. Apparently, my son even knew about this web of lies before me. Did you tell him?

I knew about the drinking, particularly after the Wheeler accident. But I actually thought he had it under control, if you can believe that.

When the lady at *The New Yorker* told me about Pop's apartment in Winchester, I honestly thought it was a mistake. Winchester? The town God forgot? I hate Winchester more than Medford, Saugus, Peabody, and Gloucester combined. He would never have lived there, I thought. Alas, I couldn't tell that my father was a drunk conman, so I guess it shouldn't be surprising that he would hole up in Winchester after he abandoned us.

But your email. That was a rude awakening. I originally put off absorbing what you wrote. "Too much anger!" I told myself. What I wanted to focus on was the fallout that would occur as a result of this information becoming public. So I had my agent whip up some painfully sincere statement to try and minimize the consequences.

As you may have noticed, the fallout has been considerable. I couldn't stop it—calls for a boycott of my book; other crap like death threats and whatnot. It's been unpleasant, to say the least.

This whole episode has brought up so many difficult memories that I'm sure you would like to forget. For me, I am just now starting to really confront this new information.

It's been hard. The fallout with Pop over Wheeler's death took me a fair amount of time to get over. It made me a terrible husband and father. It made me a terrible human.

Many of my early screenplays were actually barely concealed attempts to flush this man from my life. *The Killer Is Inside ... Your Head*, the first script I wrote, literally contained an alcoholic detective getting a lobotomy to keep from following in his father's serial killer ways (shocker that one didn't sell).

Now I am once again looking for ways to process information about a man that has continuously let me down. I'm not sure I can do it, Mom. It's too much information, built up over too many years. All the childhood memories I have of him are of this mysterious man swooping in for some fleeting moments of bonding juxtaposed with him jetting off to some life that seemed so much more exciting than ours. That life that he was supposedly living was so well developed in my mind that I never even considered an alternative career path than his. How can I just relinquish all of that to a trash can in my brain labeled "lies"?

I also can't stop thinking about Wheeler. This new information raises so many questions.

I remember always thinking that Pop liked him more—the Olympic equestrian hopeful; the Witherspoons' ticket out of obscurity. I couldn't figure out why. I was the one that emulated his career path.

Now I am left thinking that Pop liked Wheeler more because Wheeler DIDN'T follow in his fake footsteps. He didn't lap up his stupid stories about secret missions and then emulate those secret missions, first in an adolescent fantasy world and then in real life. Perhaps my successful entry into that world reminded Pop of his own shortcomings AND risked exposing his house of lies.

Also, how would Wheeler feel if he knew that the man responsible for his death never took responsibility for that? Or for any other part of his family? You know as well as I that that episode changed the course of our family. Changed the course of my life. Big time.

In hindsight, perhaps it was for the best? Perhaps my fallout with Pop after that event saved me from even more stacks of false memories and interactions with his cowardice.

I don't blame you. I hope that together we can find solace. And meanwhile, while I was writing this, I just got notified that all of my credit cards have been shut off—"suspected malicious account activity."

I'm going to try and come see you real soon. I promise. Please don't worry about me.

Always,
Strobe

# Witherspoon Leak Answers, Introduces Questions

Washington Post

Earlier today, an unknown company – Executive International Internet (EII) – released an email exchange between Ruby Witherspoon and her son Strobe. EII claimed to have more emails from Witherspoon and indicated that they would be releasing them over the coming weeks.

News outlets reporting on the leak claim that these emails add context to a number of outstanding questions regarding Witherspoon's upbringing that were brought to light in a recent *New Yorker* profile. Notably, it appears that Strobe Witherspoon was the victim of a decades-long charade by his father, Richard, who explained his frequent absences by claiming to be a CIA agent.

This is a breaking story and will be updated ...

# Executive International Internet Troll Farm Under Fire

Central News Network

AZERBAIJAN – The firm behind Rubyleaks, Executive International Internet (EII), has wiped its online presence clean. After a variety of internet sleuths began looking into their work, a trove of related social media accounts was uncovered. These accounts were found to be trafficking in a wide variety of "content," much of it related to US politics. Most recently, they had turned their attention to Strobe Witherspoon, releasing and spreading hacked emails between him and his mother. Ruby Witherspoon's senior living facility IT department has confirmed the authenticity of these emails and have announced they will launch a full investigation into the nature of the hack. Junior IT associate Leslie Stroh has been terminated for her alleged role in the incident.

Azerbaijan has also been linked to Witherspoon's earlier work at the Central Intelligence Agency, leading to speculation that the EII cyber-attacks on him and his family were initially motivated by negative portrayals of Azerbaijani criminal enterprises in Witherspoon's movie franchise *The Renditioner.*

One widely shared meme allegedly created by Ell uses a photo of a disheveled Richard Witherspoon, Strobe's father, looking over his shoulder in a confused fashion, included the text:

WHEN YOUR FAMILY'S EMAILS CONFIRM
YOUR ILLUMINATI MEMBERSHIP

Another meme suggested that Strobe's brother, Wheeler, isn't dead:

WHEELER WITHERSPOON – DEAD?
OR JUST DEEP COVER? HMMMMMMMMM.

Some memes appear to contradict the above messages in an effort to sow confusion about the Witherspoon story. A meme with a picture of Strobe Witherspoon hiding his face from a photographer included the text:

WITHERSPOON IS THE SECRET OWNER
OF EXECUTIVE INTERNATIONAL INTERNET

HE FAKED HIS OWN EMAIL LEAK

DON'T LET THE PUPPETMASTER FOOL YOU

One meme included a picture of a hooded figure with red eyes with text underneath that read:

STROBE WITHERSPOON'S DAD WORKED FOR THE CIA.

THEN STROBE "LEARNS" HIS DAD
WAS NEVER IN THE CIA.

SOUNDS COINCIDENTAL, DON'T YOU THINK?

# 28

# Mitch Witherspoon Vlog Update 2470

## Transcript

**MW:** I made it. Here I am, in an exquisite coffee shop with excellent WIFI right outside an ashram in Kolkata, Southeast India. Such a powerful place, sweaty as all getout, but you know, an insignificant price to pay to experience such majestic wonders up close and in person. Apologies in advance if there are any cows or elephants walkin' by.

Yesterday I completely shut off for most of the day. No social media posts, nothing. Ok, I jotted down some notes on a pad about today's vlog but that's it. It was bliss. Me and my mate Jürg, from Denmark – wassup Denmark viewers – we just kind of cruised around, drank a lot of tea, met some spiritual folks walkin' the streets, ate some crunchy chapati – it was my cheat day – and that was about it. Felt real good to shut down. For those of you fellow travelers out there, check out the links below for meditative tools that you can download and some other interesting tools to help you reconnect with that #zenlife while traversing this wild and wonderful world of ours. And 10% of all your purchases will be donated to the Ashram you see behind me.

I'm gonna change things up a little. Lots of comments in my feed asking me about my dad. "You keepin up with the drams?" "You talk to him at all?" "What is up with your granddad?"

Lots of questions y'all.

I know I don't talk about my father that much. Some people knew who he was, but most people didn't. People that did were pretty surprised to find out that I was his son. I get it.

The long and the short of it is my dad and I have a checkered past. My earliest memories of him are from when we used to play catch in our backyard in Virginia. When he had a job where he had to wear a tie to work. He and my mom were still together. He used to sweat through his shirt, like he was in India. Firreals. Would come home, immediately take it off and then we would watch baseball or play catch. Sounds corny, I know.

After he took off when I was like eleven, he started to seem a little more, I dunno, cranky. Angry about somethin.

When he realized I wasn't really into baseball anymore, he started giving me books to read. *Catcher*

*In The Rye*. He kept trying to get me to read that one. Couldn't get into it. He seemed disappointed.

Then I started to find my voice on social media. I wasn't very popular in school because I was short, like my mom. He couldn't understand what that was like. He was a star athlete at a fancy prep school with lots of other fancy kids. I didn't have any of that.

When I started working on my travel blog he would sometimes give me feedback. He was kind of tough on me, but fair. Some people tell me that my writing resembles his. I don't see it. But I look up to him on that and so I'm not mad at those comments. Keep em comin.

His helping me also made my mom, who I love, real mad. She hated that I "lived out loud". Ugh. That's just how I communicate! She would shut my laptop every time she walked by me. She would try and get me to go on bike rides with her. Gardening. Other stuff like that. She was against my first trip to Morocco. My dad had to intervene to get her to go for it. By then he was making a lot more money and he helped me pay for it. That was cool of him. Click here to see those old videos from three years ago. You'll notice I got a little better with the production values since then. And I've learned to be more respectful of local cultures.

I've also gotten a little better at being me. I feel like I have a lot to offer these communities I go to now. Their appreciation is a gift.

After I started really exploring that part of travel, first person perspectives on the poor and vulnerable and ways that people like me, people with privilege, can help, I really started to find my voice, and my audience. Now, when I take my camera out in a new place, I feel like I'm who I'm supposed to be. I feel connected to the beautiful souls in the remote villages I travel to while also connecting to you all out there on the Internet liking my vids and experiencing these exotic locations through my eyes. How lucky am I?!?

I've been doing this for a few years now and I'm learning so much. Doing my own research. Not just about the things I love but about the things I don't want in my life. Kind of the same way my dad did these things with his writing.

But different.

I believe that we should be moving away from the political tribalism that is tearing us all apart. All the negativity. Everyone is so phony. Power corrupts man. Politics corrupts. Phonyness corrupts. My dad, that's all he can think about and write about.

I started wondering, does my dad have the same problems with the truth that afflicted his dad. Really got me thinking... if he could be misled for so long by his dad, what about me? Could my dad have been misleading me? Has he been feeding me stories this whole time that haven't been, like, real? Is this like when your dad beats you, you beat your kid, and that kid beats their kid? Repeating the sins of your elders kinda thing?

My Buddhist guides back home encourage radical transparency. That's why I'm letting you all in on my struggle. I don't have the answers, but I'm searching for them, with you all alongside me.

Who is my dad? I think the honest answer is that I don't know. Why doesn't he talk about his dead brother? I don't know. Like, he's been knee deep in this crazy stuff for a while, maybe he doesn't even know what's true anymore.

All I'm sayin is, I'm trying to make up my own mind about things. Trying not to let the mainstream media and the politicians brainwash me like they brainwash other people. If I had let them do that I wouldn't be here, showing my audience the wonderful people of India, doing their best under really difficult circumstances.

I'm not gonna straight up agree with all of these memes and conspiracy theories out there about my family, because some of them seem kinda bonkers. But I'm also gonna keep an open mind. Stay away from these fancy magazines like *The New Yorker* that wanna control my opinions.

So stay tuned. I'll do what I can. If you think I should go back to focusing on mindfulness, seeing the world, and giving back to this great planet, comment below.

Next stop, Bangladesh. Gonna be Bangin! Sorry, that was lame.

**NEW EVIDENCE REVEALS WITHERSPOON CONNEC-
TIONS TO AZERBAIJANI CRIME FAMILY**

*The Freedom of the Press Times*

**THE WITHERSPOON CLAN IS COMING UNDONE:
WHAT YOU NEED TO KNOW**

*www.beltwaybeacon.com*

**DYSFUNCTIONAL FAMILY HAS A
DARK PAST AND SOMEHOW THAT'S NEWS**

*The Washington Skeptic*

**ARRESTS LIKELY AS THE WITHERSPOON
HOUSE OF CARDS FALLS**

*www.radicaltimesreport.ca*

# Manipulated Context Collapse Through the Utilization of Discordant Narratives: implications for social dislocation and systemic malfunction

The Journal of Sociocultural Epidemiology (JoSE)

## Abstract

**Introduction:** A preponderance of competing narratives within an anarchic communications landscape can create a perpetual state of cognitive reformulation and deviancy amplification spirals. Understanding the drivers of this phenomenon and the utility of their deployment can help mitigate the social dislocation and systemic breakdown inherent in these information ecosystems.

**Background:** Pritzky et al. posited in their landmark 2014 paper that individuals consuming arguments of sufficient complexity within an environment now known as "communication anarchy" can be induced into a "persuasion vortex" whereby otherwise rational actors form opinions devoid of the necessary contextual foundation, also known as "context collapse."

Author Strobe Witherspoon has, in recent weeks, provided a compelling test case for Pritzky analysis: a complex family dynamic, communication anarchy delivered through a multitude of unfiltered media, and demonstrable variation along the entire spectrum of Witherspoon familiarity.

**Methods:** An experimental cohort study was designed to determine the likelihood of altering the opinion of individuals with a varying level of familiarity with Witherspoon (high, medium, low) and positive and negative opinions about him (very negative, somewhat negative, neutral, somewhat positive, very positive). This was done to identify the benefits of a coordinated context collapse campaign on people with varying levels of preexisting opinions.

Initial survey was conducted after exposure to various levels of aural and visual content about Witherspoon delivered through a variety of relevant media (mainstream news, blog, podcast, memes).

One week later, participants were exposed to a coordinated context collapse campaign that offered information that was opposed to their prior week's campaign.

**Results:** A statistically significant group demonstrated notable migration in their opinions of Witherspoon.

Participants in the "somewhat negative/neutral/somewhat positive opinion" cohort migrated to the outer pole of their existing opinion (e.g., from somewhat negative to very negative) 74% of the time after the first information campaign. Participants in the "somewhat negative/neutral/somewhat positive opinion" cohort migrated to the opposite pole of their existing opinion (e.g., from somewhat negative to very positive) 16% of the time in the first week.

**Conclusion:** Exposure to initial content intended to persuade an individual to carry a more extreme opinion of Strobe Witherspoon was very effective. Participants were highly likely to take more extreme positions based on the content delivered to them, regardless of their familiarity with Witherspoon. Those in the "Low" familiarity cohort demonstrated the most extremeness of opinion shift.

One week later, exposure to a coordinated context collapse campaign that presented the opposite information was highly ineffective. Participants typically did not change their opinion or were in fact persuaded to increase the intensity of their existing opinion. A preponderance of individuals who have been inculcated with information about Strobe Witherspoon, much of it crafted to generate a specific outcome, are not cognitively inclined to reverse their opinions, even when contextual correctives are provided.

This further supports the "first mover advantage" approach for media outlets and advocacy organizations seeking to influence public discourse and build a critical mass of support around an existing narrative or opinion. It also suggests that the race to influence public opinion through the media is going to increase in both speed and certitude in the coming years, likely at the expense of nuance and accuracy.

# 31

**To: FUPATRIOTS**
**From: FEDUP1984@substack.com**
**Subject: Illuminati CONFIRMED!**

Fed Up! Email Update 4330:

Readers!!!!!! You know how I've been following this Wither-spoon story for weeks now, bringing you all the twists and turns like you've come to expect from the Fed Up! email. Well I think it's really really clear we are reaching a turning point in this story. Finally the truth we have all known for some time is starting to sink into the slower folks out there who are resistant to this kind of revolution (not you, subscribers to this email, you are the wise ones). The wheels are coming off for these Lords Of The New World Order (LOTNWO).

In recent days we've had some high-profile defections from team Witherspoon and I can tell that this is only the beginning. First, that "email hack" came out. You know I ain't that gullible and I know you guys ain't that gullible. I did the digging, and I'm gonna tell you what, Richard Witherspoon is still her husband. Boom! And that leaves only one conclusion, her whole story is a ruse, intended to throw us off Richard's scent. Sure, he is a little surprised that his mid-level apparatchik gig has been exposed. Trust me, he is still part of the plan to use the Federal

Reserve to control the money system (you know how we feel about that here at Fed Up!). He is still pretending to be some old crank when in fact he is very much an active member of the club. It's right in front of our eyes! When will everyone else recognize it? When it's too late and the Fed shuts down the money supply and the military declares Martial law?

I'll tell you who isn't too stupid to recognize it, Mitch Witherspoon. On his blog just yesterday he almost came out and admitted that his father and grandfather are part of the club. Seemed like he got a lil scared and backed off a little. But I can read people. He definitely seems like he's coming around to the shock of a lifetime – that his whole family is a hoax. That's a big deal. I remember when I found out my mom was actually my Aunt. That was a shock.

I'll tell you who else came around to the Witherspoon shock. Mitch's mother AKA Strobe's ex-wife. Why? Because she disappeared. She's a ghost. Nowhere to be found, no digital footprint. I'm guessing she got hip to this plot and they removed her like they remove everybody who gets too close to the truth.

Please show you care about these issues through your support of my anonymous donation account below. Don't forget to take my ammunition making online class. Signup is still open. Remember, it's not about who has the guns when the Armageddon comes. It's about who has the ammo.

Sign up now!

War,
Fed Up! (FU!)

# CIA Spokesperson Contradicts Witherspoon's Story

Washington Post

Langley, Virginia – Earlier today, the Central Intelligence Agency released a statement that indicated Strobe Witherspoon was terminated from his analyst position at the agency for violating policies and practices laid out in the CIA employment contract.

Director for public affairs Bernard Tripp, speaking outside the agency's headquarters in Langley, Virginia, indicated that CIA was taking the rare step of commenting on a former employee in order "to minimize false speculation and correct the public record regarding Mr. Witherspoon's employment with CIA." Tripp added that, "Mr. Witherspoon's contract was terminated for interagency clearance violations. He did not resign his position, as previously reported in certain journalistic outlets. Due to the classified nature of these violations, we are unable to provide any further details."

# Witherspoon Scripts
# Face New Scrutiny

Los Angeles Times

The hit movie franchise *The Extraordinary Renditioner* has been dormant for almost ten years. The last installment, *Renditioner: Death Rattle*, was billed as the final installment of the series (a weaker-than-expected box office all but sealed its fate).

However, new revelations about Strobe Witherspoon, the screenwriter behind the franchise, have revived interest in the films, leading to speculation that they may include references to US "black ops" or "extraordinary rendition" activities (covert transfer and interrogation of individuals outside of the United States) that remain highly classified.

Witherspoon, a former CIA analyst, has reportedly misled Hollywood, suggesting his departure from the agency was voluntary and amicable. In fact, new information reveals that he was terminated for "clearance misconduct." As a result, aficionados of the *Renditioner* franchise and intelligence analysts have been poring over his spy movies for potential links between Witherspoon's clearance abuses and the films.

Declassified files and investigative journalists in recent years have revealed details of Eastern European rendition activities that bear similarity to plot points in the first *Renditioner* film, reportedly written while Strobe was still employed at CIA. In the film, an Azerbaijani crime boss captured in the United States is suspected of planning an attack on a nuclear facility. The suspect is flown to Romania, where he is tortured and accidentally killed. Around that same time, a real Albanian crime boss with plans to release nerve gas into the New York subway system was reportedly renditioned and accidentally killed in Poland, as reported by human rights watchdogs eight years ago. Intelligence experts have suggested that the discovery of this type of screenwriting activity while Witherspoon was employed at CIA may have led to his termination. But they stress that without further information, it is difficult to know with certainty if this activity represents legitimate cause for termination or just an unfortunate coincidence.

# 34

# Clarification

## By Strobe Witherspoon

HellisOtherPeoplesBlogs.com

My tenure at the Central Intelligence Agency has recently generated renewed attention, including a vague but eyebrow-raising statement from my former employer about the circumstances of my departure. Their decision to come out of the shadows and weigh in on this matter is both surprising and disheartening.

After failing miserably at countering previous rumors, I have chosen to refrain from responding to the growing list of falsehoods pertaining to poorly articulated conspiracy theories.

Until now.

My guilt over past misdeeds combined with my desire to take back control of this shit storm have led me to break my silence.

The truth is that I was fired from the CIA. Not because I disclosed any juicy extraordinary rendition secrets – all of the general details about those black ops were already well known when I wrote the first *Renditioner* script.

It was because I used my connections at the Massachusetts FBI to change the details of my brother's death. And I got caught. And I got fired. I did it because I thought I was protecting myself and my father from scrutiny. We both supposedly chose lives in the shadows and we both therefore preferred to keep our names off of coroner's reports and news items. The coroner's report was never fixed. Internal Affairs and the coroner's office probably decided it would draw too much attention and just left it as is. Who knows.

I never told my father what I did. I thought I was protecting him. Turns out he wasn't worth protecting. Turns out I am more of an idiot than I realized. Turns out there is nothing I can do to prevent people from pouring fuel on the fire that is my dysfunctional family.

My hope is that this information will help quell the speculation.

# 35

# The Daily Dose Morning Show

---

Transcript

---

[MUSIC INTRO]

**FP:** You're listenin to the Daily Dose Morning Show and I'm Forrest Poundstone. Richard Witherspoon is in the studio today. We have questions. But first, a message from our sponsor, Colon Cure. Is your colon more like a semicolon...

**FP:** ...we're back. Richard, thanks for joining us. My producer tells me you aren't a big fan of interviews, would that be a fair statement?

**RW:** Sure.

**FP:** Because you don't want to go on the record?

**RW:** Because I don't trust these types of things. I listen to your show. So I thought you would be OK.

**FP:** Appreciate it. There's no gotcha going on in here.

**RW:** Yeah.

**FP:** So is everyone insane or are we starting to get too close to the truth about the radical left's culture war agenda?

**RW:** There's a lot of stuff going on out there that we haven't been told about. And there are smart people like you and others that are doing the research and calling them out. We know about the big ones, like the Rothchilds – a lot of them are still out there, but they don't use that last name, cuz they're sneaky. But also, the smaller ones, the ones that are in the shadows, inside the government, inside the tech companies, your phone, my phone. They're in there. My son, that's a different story.

**FP:** How is your son a different story?

**RW:** He just is.

**FP:** Care to elaborate?

**RW:** Well.

**FP:** Isn't he connected to the deep state?

**RW:** I don't know.

**FP:** If anybody would know, wouldn't it be you?

**RW:** I don't have any information.

**FP:** Some of my listeners think otherwise.

**RW:** I know. My background. Was I a spy?

**FP:** Correct. You ready to set the record straight?

**RW:** I am.

**FP:** Great. I'm all ears.

[PAUSE]

**RW:** I was never a spy.

**FP:** Isn't that what a spy would say?

**RW:** It is. And I've used that move before. But I wanted to come on here to tell you, to your face, a man I spend almost every morning with for four hours, that I made it up.

**FP:** Why?

**RW:** You read my ex's email, right?

**FP:** So you just wanted your son to be proud of you? You wanted to hide your drinking and galivanting?

**RW:** I'm embarrassed by it. It was a dumb, stupid thing to do. I was going off the rails at home. It started out small. Then Strobe got really into the charade. Then I got really into it. I wanted him to love me. Respect me. I was ashamed of who I'd become and so I became someone else. I actually started to do a lot of reading about the CIA just to stay ahead of the story. About the history, the people they recruited from the Ivy leagues, the so-called "intellectual class." Which is why I now know what they're up to. It's all a sham. And more people need to know about it. But back then I just used those books to tell my son mysterious stories. He loved it so much.

**FP:** And he never found out?

**RW:** Sounds like he didn't.

**FP:** Even when he was working for the CIA?

**RW:** I think he thought I was in real deep, where the records don't tell you everything. Who knows? Maybe he didn't look too hard? People will believe a lot if they want it bad enough.

**FP:** Well…

**RW:** It's called motivated reasoning.

**FP:** OK, so now what do you think of him? This book that he wrote about the savior of this great country. The POTUS with the Mostus.

**RW:** I'm not gonna mince words on this. The crap that he peddles makes me sick. The thought that people associate me with those crazy ideas makes me want to punch him in the face. That he could attack our former president and his ex-wife, the best things that have happened to our country since the Red Sox broke the curse of the bambino… just makes me…

**FP:** You wish he stayed in the CIA?

**RW:** That's a hard one. Who knows what he saw there that turned him into what he is now. I bet it was some crazy sh—

**FP:** Easy there. This isn't that kind of show.

**RW:** Look, we stopped talking around the time he left the agency.

**FP:** Around the time his brother died. Your son.

**RW:** I told your producer we aren't talking about that.

**FP:** So you can't confirm that Wheeler's death and your fallout with Strobe were related. That Strobe tried to cover up your negligence surrounding Wheeler's death and then got fired for it?

[PAUSE]

**FP:** Did you know that Strobe got fired?

**RW:** I just found out.

**FP:** Do you believe his new story about that?

**RW:** I don't know what to believe. Maybe he already knew he wanted to be a Hollywood elitist that spouts nonsense for fancy city folk and the agency wasn't doing it for him. Maybe he tried to hide Wheeler's death so he would get found out and fired.

**FP:** Couldn't he have just quit?

**RW:** I don't know! Who knows what he was thinking. He seemed intent on becoming a Hollywood big shot, that's all I know. And that's enough for me to not trust him anymore.

**FP:** Hollywood does have quite a hold on our youths. Those images of pulsating flesh, cavorting in their orgies with their narcotics, the kids and their sanctimonious parents eating it up in their genderless pant dresses.

**RW:** Exactly. It's ruining us all. And he just went out there and bent over for them. I still can't believe that a son of mine would do something like that.

**FP:** So do you talk to him at all?

**RW:** No.

**FP:** You talk to other people in your family? Your brother Horace? He's also out there giving his opinion on this situation, and on you.

**RW:** We exchange holiday cards.

**FP:** So you're not close.

**RW:** He's been fully inducted into the New England chapter of the limousine liberal hall of fame. He doesn't even like the Red Sox. Never did. I think Strobe may have gotten some of that from him. Horace saw the opportunity to infect Strobe with his pretentious crap. He treated him like the son he never had.

**FP:** Does that bother you?

**RW:** Does it bother me that my brother brainwashed my son? Yes it does.

**FP:** Have you told Horace that?

**RW:** Like I said, we're not that close. Every now and then he thinks he needs to call and quote unquote check on me. But that's about it.

**FP:** Sounds condescending.

**RW:** It is.

**FP:** You don't seem like you need people checking in on you.

**RW:** I don't. I need a new knee and I may have skin cancer but I'm gonna be fine. Haven't had a drink in five years.

**FP:** Congrats.

**RW:** You helped me get sober. I haven't missed your show in, I dunno, maybe three years. I used to set my clock to it back in the day. Now I can listen to it on my computer. I feel like I know you.

**FP:** Appreciate it.

**RW:** I don't talk to too many people that aren't already fans of yours.

**FP:** Smart.

**RW:** It's no use. When I hear people talking about how the government is going to solve all our problems, I just want to shake them. The government is our problem!

**FP:** Except the military.

**RW:** Yes.

**FP:** When will the coasts understand that?

**RW:** Maybe when they join the military.

**FP:** Exactly. Skin in the game.

**RW:** It's so tiring. All those immigrants I used to teach English to, they never even understood how they were being used by the left to win elections. The demographic warfare is gonna destroy you and me if we aren't careful. It's all out there. You know the left don't want Mexicans and Muslims in our country any more than we do. I feel sorry for these immigrants to be honest. They're just gonna get tossed to the side once they're no longer necessary.

**FP:** They think these people can just come in, get citizenship, then take over our government because they outnumber us? That's not democracy. That's kleptocracy. They are stealing our government from the rightful owners – the original settlers of these great United States.

**RW:** I think we should pass a law to keep them from voting.

**FP:** Then we'll see how much those liberals care about immigration.

**RW:** Would be great to see the looks on their smug faces when they realize their pretend campaign to like immigrants didn't work.

**FP:** People are set in their ways. They refuse to listen to people like you.

**RW:** I think my son could be convinced. Maybe you could get him on the show.

**FP:** We've been trying. His "people" are like a brick wall.

**RW:** That's part of the problem. The bubble he's in.

**FP:** Only thirty seconds left Richard, anything else you'd like to say...

**RW:** I really just came here to clear my name. I did a bad thing telling my son a story about me that wasn't true. I never thought it would go this far. Strobe, if you hear this, I miss you. I know I don't often show it. And I know we're different. But let's fix this together.

**FP:** You think he'll respond to you?

**RW:** I don't know.

**FP:** Are your ingrown hairs embarrassing? The new Zappemout laser treatment from Rumple Smoovskin is the answer...

# 36

**To: FUPATRIOTS**
**From: FEDUP1984@substack.com**
**Subject: The Daily Dose Is Dead To Me**

FED UP! EMAIL UPDATE 4331:

So it's come to this. I can no longer stand by and watch as another bastion of our army falls.

Yesterday, we finally heard from Richard, "Tricky" Witherspoon. It was on *The Daily Dose*, a radio show that I used to listen to. It's online if you need to hear it. But let me make a suggestion: don't.

I wish the Dose had opened its eyes to the obvious reality. "Tricky" still up to his dirty tricks. Claimed to have never been a secret agent for the US government when we all know that that is demonstrably false. See any of my previous email updates for incontrovertible evidence. Message to Tricky, facts don't care about your lies.

We know he's gonna pretend to be estranged from his son and his wife, WHO HE IS STILL MARRIED TO. And some people are going to eat that nonsense up.

But the FU! army is not some people. I didn't think the Dose was either. But et tu Daily Dose? Or is there something else going on here that we don't know about? Are there ghosts in your machine? Are you too cozy with your corporate sponsors? You can't just let someone like Tricky Witherspoon onto your show and uncritically let him pedal his lies.

We know what to do. Let the Dose know that it's not cool to give these people platforms to just run their mouths without getting challenged by the truth. Let Richard Witherspoon know that you aren't gonna just leave him alone anymore. And let Strobe know that his secret games that he is playing with the deep state and the New World Order crew are no longer secret. By whatever means necessary FU! crew.

War,
FU!

# 37

**From: Ruby Witherspoon <ruby.witherspoon@aol.com>**
**To: Strobe Witherspoon <swither@wthrspnllc.com>**
**SUBJECT: Missing You**

Dearest Strobe,

Oh the mess. Needless to say, Leslie from the computer center has been terminated. Rarely do I find my judge of character to be so woefully inaccurate. But alas, Leslie deserves a swift kick where the sun does not shine for stealing our emails and selling them. She was nothing but kind to me, always making sure I was comfortable and sitting at the "good" computer (which I now realize was really just the computer that she could use to look at my emails after I was gone). I'm clenching my teeth as I write this (which my dentist says I should stop). Bad behavior from people that you trust is not something I get over easily.

But there seems to be a lot of bad behavior going around these days. They keep playing pranks on the front desk here. Some of them are juvenile, others are reprehensible.

Apparently, somebody pretending to be you keeps trying to get in. When they don't let him in the fake Strobe will start ranting something about mind control or something. Then they get escorted out. The center has added an extra security guard to their payroll I am sorry to say.

Another time, they called in a bomb threat on our building. We all had to evacuate. It was cold out and many of the other people in the center were visibly angry at me when they learned that this prank was because of me.

One person was able to get access to our big TV that sits outside the recreation room.

This is what they typed into the TV:

1:30 PM – BINGO FOLLOWED BY DEATH TO ALL LIZARD WITHERSPOONS

5:00 PM – SEMINAR: PREVENTING HYPERTENSION RUBY WITHERSPOON'S SON IS BUTT RAPING AMERICA

7:30 PM – SEINFELD MARATHON (JEWISH CRAP)

Disgraceful. And not even a little humorous. Do you agree?

Some people here have been reading a lot of the news online about you and seem like they may be believing some of it. I'm starting to think that giving them access to all these news stories may not be such a great idea. Some of them are, how shall I say it, not exactly the sharpest wits of their generations—or if they were, those days have passed them by. I have pretty much stopped reading the news because I can't tell what's real anymore, but that doesn't stop others here from printing things out and showing them to me.

Their questions are always so fraught with faulty logic and manipulation by these online news sites.

With all of this attention comes a lot of questions about Richard. Unfortunately, I don't have all the answers. I know that deep down there is a sensitive man in there that has suffered indignity throughout this ordeal. But I am not of the position that we should continue to protect him from the inevitable questions that have been arising. And he seems to be feeding into this frenzy by going on these radio shows and posting on the Facebook.

I die a little each time Wheeler comes up. Most hurtful are the questions from people here that suggest that he isn't dead but just working "deep cover" in the "deep state", whatever that means. Or that he never really existed but was used as a false identity for you when you were working for the government. Do these people even understand how much that hurts?

I'm sorry Strobelight, I shouldn't burden you with all of this. I am going to continue to do my best for us. You are all I have left now. I don't care if the whole Internet knows that (don't worry I took an online class about end-to-end email encryption to ward off the hackers).

I will be strong, you can count on that. In the meantime, I hope you are able to find some peace in all of this madness. I am hopeful that it will soon be over.

Always,
Ruby

# 38

# THE BOOK OF STROBE:
## The Fifth Cycle of the Hellfire Prophecy

**by A. Nona Mouse**

---

Introduction

---

*"The Quintasm is upon us. Those that resist will be
relegated to servitude. Those that embrace will be
rewarded" – Strobe Witherspoon, son of Richard*

Much speculation has occurred regarding the inner workings of the shadow systems to which we are all beholden. **False prophets** and opportunistic zealots are committed to your perpetual enslavement through the art of distraction. They do this to keep what I am about to reveal out of sight.

The significance of this book cannot be understated. If the Hellfire Prophecy is realized those who are not properly positioned will be destined for servitude. So will their children. And their children's children.

This information comes directly from the **inner sanctum**: the Witherspoon lineage. Many people don't want you to know this information. They think you might use it to try to thwart the prophecy or replace those who stand to gain from it. They have worked hard to keep this manifesto out of your hands. The publishing industry has refused to recognize its significance, so I am forced to self-publish. The mainstream media has filled the airwaves with stories of intrigue hedonism and violence to distract and disarm us to the reality at hand. Hence they will not cover this I promise you and that will be evidence of their collusion with these forces. Disregard all of that. Allow me to explain…

### *What is the Quintasm?*

The Quintasm is the **fifth and final cycle of the Hellfire Prophecy**. To trigger this cycle there will be a messenger that will reveal Himself. That person is **Strobe Witherspoon, son of Richard**. I have come to learn this through years of research. One strand of that research turned up the quote I provided above via the decoding of Strobe's public messages. These messages are clear to those who understand the code. Those who do not understand it think it is just the work of some silly inconsequential fiction writer. That is precisely why I must shroud my true identity in secrecy. Just typing these words out puts me at risk. Their tools of **subjugation** are strong. They have text scraping technology that can be implanted on any computer connected to the Internet. Which is why I have written this on a decommissioned desktop from 2006.

For those that have made it this far, proceed with caution as you **ingest the nutrients** of this forbidden fruit. Behold: the Book of Strobe.

This Book has taken many years to complete it bears the scars of a circuitous path filled with detours both horrible and transcendent. Without such a journey however I would not have been able to collect the perspective and wisdom necessary to alert the world to this fifth and final cycle of the Hellfire

Prophecy and to confirm the identity of the figure that will trigger this transition—Strobe Witherspoon, son of Richard.

Pay attention. You will be rewarded.

This Book is laid out in meticulous fashion and will be presented as follows:

### Chapters 1–4: The First Four Cycles

In these chapters of The Book, you will learn of the eras— or "cycles"—that prepared our land for the **Reckoning**.

The first cycle is about society's embrace of **religious doctrine**. The belief systems that were born of these activities and the struggles for human survival that ensued were instrumental in securing the necessary transition to the next cycle.

The second cycle focuses on the **political systems** that emerged from the foundation laid during cycle one. This second cycle occurred midway through the last millennia with the advent of modern democracy, nation-states, and the international system as we know it. The struggle for power and autonomy that it created persists today. The analysis of said struggle proliferates within the "hallowed" halls of political science and history departments around the world and filters out onto the news channels conference stages non-governmental organizations think tanks and dinner tables of the global elite. This analysis façade has been designed to present an impression of self-determination and "the science of politics" that is used to suppress dissent and keep the have-nots in the dark about their exploitation.

The third cycle is about the **technology** that has been used to oppress the masses. These increasingly destructive tools of physical war and civilizational mind control have entrenched the tribalistic urges of different groups and created an environment of perpetual warfare and resource battles which in turn distracted and destroyed any potential revolutionary underclass. This third cycle was born out of such early advances as the printing press and overlapped with cycle two and eventually overtook it during the era of the great twentieth century global hegemony contests (World War One, World War Two, and the Cold War).

The fourth cycle. The cycle in which we currently find ourselves. This is a transition to a new battleground: **the war for our minds** waged vis-à-vis the systems that explained above that have come before it. These previous contests of faith ideology and property laid the groundwork for a mind battle of almost incomprehensible complexity hidden from all but the most enlightened and focused humans. Humans who understand this current environment fall into two categories: those who benefit from it and their ilk and those—including myself—who are destined to fight this dark prophecy. These fighters of this prophecy are the only ones that can thwart the transition to the fifth and final cycle. **The Quintasm**. More on that later.

### Chapters 5-9: The Witherspoons

These chapters will lay out in painstaking detail the journey of the Witherspoon family, a lineage destined from the founding of the United States to play a central role in the Hellfire Prophecy. We will learn about **Eldridge Witherspoon** and his rise to patrician noblesse during the era of the founding fathers. From there we will fast forward to his grandson Richard Sr. a man destined to an ignominious life of little regard. But he fulfilled the mission of his father and his father's father: he bore a son. That son was Richard Jr. the man for whom the keys to the deep state and all of its riches would be bequeathed. Richard Jr.—AKA "Tricky"—who would go on to construct the levers of the modern day New World Order is a man of almost unparalleled skill in the deception and misdirection crafts.

**Richard Witherspoon Jr. was not an underachieving alcoholic like his father**. When he received word that it was time to construct the architecture of the modern deep state he was ready. He created an agency so secret so transnational in nature that no paper trail of it exists. Anybody who speaks about it to the uninitiated is immediately **killed or lobotomized**. While Richard was doing this he constructed a counter-narrative about himself of such brilliance (and inspired by that of his father) that the world believed that he was not the keeper of the keys to the secret kingdom of plutocrats. They believed he was a failed baseball player and alcoholic separated from his wife and living a life of unremarkable solitude in Maine.

The world was also led to believe that his son Strobe had abandoned his professional destiny and was a middling writer of satirical fiction who nominally criticized the exact community in which he was a principal figure.

If ever there was a time for this specific quote, it is now: **"The greatest trick the devil ever pulled was convincing the world he didn't exist."** (Keyser Soze, *The Usual Suspects*)

And then there was **Wheeler Witherspoon**. This **mystical creature** provides the missing piece of the puzzle. As I will show in my research of texts from earlier generations the trigger for the fifth cycle has been determined to be the sacrifice of an inner sanctum male via a **secret pagan horse ritual** known as "equestracide." Strobe and Richard were all too happy to comply with this instruction in order to secure their primacy within the organizational architecture of the Hellfire Prophecy. They were also instrumental in destroying any evidence of Wheeler's equestrian accident. They never spoke of it even within their own immediate family. And there is no record of the "accident" anywhere. No press reports. No mention of it on the death certificate. Nothing. Coincidence? I think not.

### Chapters 10-13: The Journey to Enlightenment and the Preconditions of Quintasm

The research for this book has taken me to the brink of insanity and back but my resolve never faltered. The stakes were too high. Which is why in these final chapters I lay out my meticulous journey to better understanding the factors that will trigger the fifth cycle. **The QUINTASM.**

I have built this understanding from long-discarded oral histories to secret messages written in code via encyclopedias to the iconographic instructions found within the currencies around the world.

In these chapters I will lay out in great detail how I came to learn that Strobe and Richard were informed early in their respective lives of the looming **"Call to Equestracide."**

It is now twenty years since the horse-based sacrifice of Wheeler Witherspoon. Almost all of the **preconditions for the transition to the fifth cycle** (the Quintasm) have been met. They include:

- the creation of an **opaque global trading system** that benefits those who control the levers of power and confuses the many who do not have access to said levers;

- **manufactured public health crises** that purport to

threaten our well-being but are actually elite power plays to enslave the masses and accumulate wealth;

- **manufactured food shortages** to starve potential revolutionaries on the periphery of the international trading system and keep them too weak and distracted to fight back;

- the preponderance of a **sedentary lifestyle** within the core of the world system that limit the fighting capabilities of potential revolutionaries;

- the creation of **democratic governance norms** that present citizens with a false sense of self-determination and political inclusivity;

- the proclamation of **martial law** in the United States and the forced labor of all those who resist the coming Quintasm. This precondition has not yet been met.

- The final precondition will emerge once the above preconditions have been met. It will be the wholesale **confiscation of the tools of revolution** and the silencing of voices like mine that wish to inform the uninformed of the coming Hellfire.

When the preconditions are met the fifth and final cycle of the prophecy will commence, marking the wholesale subjugation of the human race carried out by an elite strata of "enabled" humans claiming complete ownership of their "subjects".

**This is not summer camp** we are talking about. Subjects will be controlled by their enabled captors via the tools of physical technological spiritual and psychological control that they acquired during the previous four cycles. There will be no sixth cycle.

**The human race is at a crossroads.**

I have done the research.

If you are told that you are safe don't believe it. If you are told you are "chosen" don't believe it. If you are told that you can't win this battle don't believe it. All of those tactics are just thinly veiled "subject control" methods that must be defended against.

Only together through **vigilance** and **determination** will we be able to alter the course of history and **take back our futures from our aspirational elitist overlords.**

Fight on.

A. Nona Mouse (ANM).

# 39

# I Will Not Lose The War On Reality To Idiots

## By Strobe Witherspoon

HellisOtherPeoplesBlogs.com

The Book of Strobe has been released. And now apparently it has found a following.

Oh no.

Good job everybody.

Interestingly enough, this "manifesto" is correct on one point: there is a war going on for our minds. Don't misunderstand me: that is not a confirmation of the "fourth cycle of Hellfire Prophecy." Far from it. It is a condemnation of the people on the Internet who are no longer attached to the real world and promulgate outrageous garbage in order to avoid their own sad realities.

To those people engaging in this tinfoil hat nonsense: I get it. On many fronts—employment, health, romance, dignity—you have been let down. American society seems to be leaving you behind. But that is no excuse for what you're doing. These rabbit holes may provide short-term distractions, but they will not protect you from the realization that life is no longer providing you the real-world purpose that you crave.

To those who don't actually believe in this nonsense but take great pleasure in "pwning" elites, RINOs, SJWs, bankers, globalists, or whatever vague category of people has gotten you riled up today: get over your self. That momentary joy you take in other people's pain has real-life consequences. Those dopamine jolts are going to run out at some point, and all you're going to be left with is your own failure and irresponsibility staring at you in the mirror.

Or even worse: we will be left with a society full of dumb shits like you perpetuating whatever false narrative they want in order to justify society's final lap around the sewer drain of stupidity.

You repulsive entitled mouth breathers need to stop. Maybe you should get a job. Or a life.

But now, a confession: I fear that my father may be one of you. His underwhelming path led him to do and say many things that were not based in reality. His refusal to take responsibility for his actions cost him his family.

He is reaping what he hath sowed.

The sad, ironic truth is that his lies many years ago may have now cost him the one community he had left. If this Hellfire Prophecy were about anybody else, I'd suspect he would be leading the charge to prevent the Quintasm. Maybe he would start a Facebook group about it and stockpile his Meals Ready-to-Eat.

It must break his heart to be on the wrong side of this debacle.

So, take pride, all you Internet trolls and trollettes: you may not be able to break me, but you have almost certainly broken the spirit of a feeble old man who shares your paranoia and refusal to take responsibility. For the last decade, he has depended almost entirely on the anger machinery of the Internet to distract him from his own failings. You people took that from him. Take a bow.

But let me reiterate: I am not going away. I will not curtsy to your online harassment efforts. I will not recede from view. I will not surrender to your fantastical urges for power and relevance. You people don't deserve my attention. You people disgust me. You people need to go.

# VITAL Books Shelves FLOTUS

The Daily News

After weeks of rumors, VITAL Books announced it will not move forward with Strobe Witherspoon's novel *FLOTUS: a memoir*. VITAL is reportedly in negotiations to sever all ties with the author after a blog post by Witherspoon was seen as "exacerbating the issue" and "increasing the intensity of the boycott." Sales data suggest the VITAL boycott doubled after Witherspoon's entry on HellisOtherPeoplesBlogs.com was posted.

Witherspoon's post was widely attacked for its condescending and confrontational tone as well as its use of the term "you people." Calls to take the post down went unheeded.

With business buckling from the boycott, VITAL stated, "We can no longer ignore our fiduciary responsibility to our shareholders and threaten our relationships with our extraordinary roster of best-selling authors. We wish Mr. Witherspoon the best of luck in his future endeavors."

# In Which I Respond To The Book Of Strobe Controversy

### (read all the way through for a special bonus)

**By Amber Witherspoon**

---

Bookjacketquotes.com

---

In my seven years in the book publishing industry, providing writers with best-in-class PR and communications services unavailable via traditional publishing houses, I have never seen anything like this. To answer my father Horace's question (click here for that), "No, I don't think we can read anymore." At least that was my conclusion after skimming this *Book Of Strobe* that has the Internet up in arms and now seems to have resulted in the cancellation of my cousin's next novel, his finest work yet.

First off, regarding this *Book of Strobe*, I probably don't need to tell the people who read this, but just to be clear, there's nothing even resembling the truth in any of the pages of that rambling mess of a manifesto.

Also, I'm not a stickler for grammar, but seriously, does this A. Nona Mouse person understand commas? To be honest, I wonder if English is his/her first language. I'm not casting aspersions on foreigners, but I will say this: If you're going to make up a fabricated apocalyptic prophecy about my family, USE PROPER ENGLISH!

I'm sorry, but the degradation of the English language is not something I take lightly. It pains me to the core of my being, which also, as it were, includes a business that started out with book blurbs and has grown into a full service dynamo that has taken the industry by storm, but which also depends on the hard work and keen intellectual insights of humans that know that writing is their calling, an activity that burns in them so deep that they are willing to toil for years in obscurity, in an intellectual and economic wilderness, a cold, barren wasteland that would make mere mortals retreat to safer, warmer environs. For it is the fire that burns inside them that keeps them warm during the cold nights where the only thing for them to feed on is a cold stew of fear, insecurity, bounced rent checks, and the vocal disappointment of their parents, who constantly tell them to just go to law school and stop with this pipe dream already.

For the record, my father never pushed me to go to law school. He suggested I think about focusing a little bit more on the business side of the publishing world. It was a bitter pill to swallow, I must admit. He never openly compared me to Cousin Strobe, but I could tell that's what he was doing. His feedback on my work was always something like, "could use more tension", "maybe you need to spend a little more time in this character's head", or "but what's the story *really* about?"

I sometimes wonder if he would have treated the son that he never had like that.

I've come a long way since then, channeling my love for the written word into a lucrative and fulfilling business. Click on the ABOUT tab for my rates and some of my work helping writers get the best book jacket quotes in the business, among other things.

I am not giving up on *FLOTUS: A Memoir.* I believe you will thank me for my commitment to this piece of bittersweet satirical writing, if only you could read it for yourselves and bask in its irreverent, poignant take on a topic that is sure to be a conversation piece at water coolers across the country.

Which brings me to my special surprise. Against the wishes of some people who shan't be named here I give to you a very special *FLOTUS* excerpt. It's an acerbic yet heartfelt look at one woman's quest for credibility in a male dominated world (that has nothing to do with assassination plots or apocalypses!). This excerpt, with its subtle and sardonic exploration of what it means to be a hard-working, intellectually curious, and yes, attractive woman in the modern age, felt like it was speaking directly to me.

# Chapter 5: Hear Me Roar

(from *FLOTUS: a memoir*)

We live in a world where intense scrutiny of the physical self is the norm. It became ingrained in me from an early age that how a woman looks takes precedence over what a woman thinks.

*He* used to tell me that. "As long as you got it going on there (points to my chest), and there (points to my rear end), it doesn't really matter what you got going on up there (points to my head)."

When my sister suggested that she would like to continue to pursue her medical degree after college, my father told her, "It's fine if that's what you want to do, my child, but don't let it get in the way of starting a family. Papa wants some grandchildren, and you aren't getting any younger." She was twenty-one.

Maybe you do always end up marrying your father.

Before the accident, Petra confided in me that she had started to talk about children with her boyfriend, who was six months away from becoming a doctor. "I can take some time off if necessary. Perhaps we'll get married next year, have a child, and then I can resume my studies."

I wasn't entirely convinced she meant what she said about resuming her studies. I'll never know.

Little did I realize that I was just as imprisoned by the gender roles that my sister had succumbed to in her relationship. Petra was selling her body to a man who was going to make "an honest woman out of her," as the American saying goes. I was selling my body on the runway. In return, I got money. Petra, her prize would be the right to bear her husband a child or two or six.

We were both shackled by our life choices. When I finally stopped modeling in my mid-thirties, I had mixed feelings. On the one hand, I had been a slave to a gang of ogling Neanderthals in tailored suits with a fondness for long hugs. On the other hand, that slavery did work out for me in the financial department (which I guess makes it not exactly like slavery).

What did I have to show for it? I asked myself. Some magazine covers. Some passport stamps. An intense desire to never go to another secret party in Saudi Arabia.

After much soul searching and more than a few years of severe depression, I had an epiphany.

I saw it very clearly. The next chapter in my life was about sharing. Sharing the business decisions that worked out for me and the decisions that didn't; the great meals and the disappointing ones; and the intellectual insights of a woman who had freed herself from the economic servitude and paralyzing corruption that shackled my family back in Slovakia.

This is where my heart is at today. Showing the world that I am not now nor was I ever just arm candy. Letting others learn through me, in areas like interior design, where I have developed a unique flare for marrying the proto-maximalist with the practical in large urban penthouses. Or, in the area of culinary arts and hospitality, where my sophisticated palate and experience hosting large dinner parties can help people who are frequently overwhelmed by the daunting and opaque world of high-end catered cuisine. Or, exploring the complexities of the human form. It is through my paintings, of the male and female body, nude, exposed, candid, that I can subvert society's preconceptions of beauty. I can put our superficial obsessions under a microscope in a way that grapples with humanity's inherent contradictions and imperfections. It took me many years of subjugation as a model and a wife to discover this and to let it inform my art.

I recognize that I never became the world-famous supermodel that the ambitious, narrow-minded seventeen-year-old in Slovakia fantasized about. But I did okay. And I can now use my past to help inform my contributions to the global conversation around ourselves and our bodies. In this new environment, I call the shots.

I am thankful for all those who influenced me along the way, including my father and my ex-husband. They showed me the flaws in the human race that I can now put into my work. That perspective has helped me present a layered critique of gender norms and mass media in a unique and compelling manner. I am honored and humbled to display some of my nude model portraits in this book, but I would also strongly recommend you seek them out in their natural habitat, a museum. That is where the power of those portraits lies. I am hopeful that a museum tour will finally become a reality for me, thus increasing my exposure and acceptance as an artist.

To be clear, I am still growing, still learning, still pushing myself. I am eager to share more of this work with the world and I am hopeful that the readers of this memoir will join me in this journey.

I am ready for the world to see me.

I am FLOTUS, hear me roar.

*(end of excerpt)*

**To: FUPATRIOTS**
**From: FEDUP1989@substack.com**
**Subject: Pondering Quintasm**


FED UP! EMAIL UPDATE 4332:

FU! crew, we been receiving a lot of questions about this Hellfire Prophecy. We hear ya loud and clear. That is why we have been doing our research, carefully weighing the merits of this substantial piece of work.

After much deliberation, we have to admit that we appreciated and agreed with a lot of this manifesto—particularly the parts about elite efforts to manufacture crises so they can suppress the masses and accumulate wealth. We been talking about that for a while. Those power hoarders are still congratulating themselves for their scheme from a few years ago. So many sheeple fell for that one but not us here at FU!

But, and this is a crucial but, we have some questions and concerns.

A lot of the facts provided in the manifesto felt like they were pushing the limits of our known universe. For instance, the quote from the Introduction:

> *"The Quintasm is upon us. Those that resist will be relegated to servitude. Those that embrace will be rewarded" – Strobe Witherspoon, son of Richard*

This was reportedly ascertained by using a decoding device referred to in the endnotes as "ouiji 2.0". Is A. Nona Mouse's (ANMs) saying that a special new Ouiji board was used to decode this quote? Keep in mind this wasn't the only quote that supposedly used this system:

> *"We are all destined to destruction during the transition to the fifth cycle, except those that heed the words of this book."*

Seriously? A ouiji board told you that? For background, I have experience with Ouiji and at one point was a member of a number of online Ouija communities. I know what I'm talking about here. If I don't know about this Ouiji 2.0 stuff I'm going to have to say that it sounds fishy. My brothers and sisters in the Ouiji community that I reached out to also agree with me on this point.

Look, I'm not going to say that we here at the FU! email update don't believe ANM is fighting the good fight. I just wonder whether this manifesto takes the focus away from the key source of the global cabal–the Federal Reserve. We can't lose sight of this menace. Which is why the Book of Strobe feels like it might be, dare I say, a distraction. Not one mention in the 900 pages of the Book of Strobe—not even the section on the global trading system!–of how the US

Fed, in cahoots with other central banks around the world, is the centerpiece for the global domination campaign of the sneaky, usurious bankers and financiers that are keeping us all in dire financial straits. Can I get an Amen?

Regardless, my team and I here at FU! are going to keep researching and updating you. Quintasm or no Quintasm, we will not waver in the face of this existential threat.

War,
FED UP! (FU!).

**To: FUPATRIOTS**
**From: QUINTASMCONTRA533@substack.com**
**Subject: THE BOOK OF STROBE IS REAL**

Dear Fed Up! Subscribers:

This is Jotham, the (former) IT administrator at FU! I took the liberty (LIBERTY!) of borrowing the FU! Email list. Ah fuck it. I took that shit. Because you need to know the truth (and I don't take shit from no one, not counting email lists, I take those.). The FU! email update has been compromised. Our once fearless leader Steve is wavering in the face of the obvious truth: the Book of Strobe is the guidance we have been waiting for. So I set up this new newsletter to keep you all informed and up to date about the next stage in the Quintasm uprising (it's gonna be HUUUGGGEEE). I am leading this new group called the QCs (the Quintasm Contras). Stay tuned for more updates (COMING REAL SOON). And stay strong, we will need all of your strength to reverse the Hellfire Prophecy (and please let your email system know that this is NOT SPAM).

RISE UP,
QC Jotham

**From: Strobe Witherspoon <swither@wthrspnllc.com>**
**To: Ruby Witherspoon <ruby.witherspoon@aol.com>**
**SUBJECT: re: Missing You**

Hi, Mom,

First off, to answer your earlier question, no, none of those pranks on your rec room TV screen were funny. Please offer my apologies to the others at the center that had to endure that.

Secondly, thank you for employing end-to-end encryption on your emails. I would say, however, that for now we should just assume that people are going to do whatever it takes to read our emails and misrepresent them to satisfy their own agendas. That said, I don't really care that much anymore. Since they cancelled my book, I officially have nothing to hide.

Has Dad reached out to you? I haven't heard from him. I have to assume he is handling this with characteristic rage. Presuming he can still walk, I'm gonna guess there is a lot of pacing and nail gnawing going on. I guess I can take credit for that, which, hooray?

I may reach out to him, unless you think that is a bad idea.

Out of everything that's happening, Wheeler getting dragged into this makes me the angriest. I can't even imagine how it makes Pop feel, seeing as he is the one that killed him.

There, I wrote it. I'm not going to let myself get caught up in this whodunnit about Wheeler's death and be forced to continue the lie that tore our family apart.

However, I also think that there may be something Pop and I can do to make this go away. Surely the more the world sees him for who he is, the less they will be willing to believe he is leading some misbegotten march toward Armageddon through a life of clandestine malfeasance. Right? Is that crazy? Am I crazy?

I'm thinking about relocating for a little while to get away from all of this. Maybe I'll be able to come out to see you. I'll make sure the people at the desk know it's me when I arrive.

Good luck at the 1:30 PM BINGO FOLLOWED BY DEATH TO ALL ILLUMINATI WITHERSPOONS activity. Yup, still not funny.

Best,
Strobe

# 45

# PRESS RELEASE
# FOR IMMEDIATE RELEASE

## CONTACT: STEVEN TORKERSON

### EMAIL: thetorkenator411@nra.org

**NRA RESPONDS TO HELLFIRE PROPHECY**

Fairfax, Virginia – The National Rifle Association (NRA) strenuously denies any role in the online publication *The Book of Strobe: the fifth cycle of the Hellfire Prophecy.*

Internet rumors have suggested the NRA, in conjunction with an Azerbaijani troll farm, authored this manifesto to spur sales in firearms and related merchandise. The NRA Leadership Team asserts that it is made up of law-abiding individuals who are committed to the well-being of the citizens of the United States of America and the security of the homeland. It did not and will not engage in efforts to sway opinion about gun ownership through the use of opaque partnerships with anonymous individuals, unknown organizations, and purveyors of speculative fictional narratives such as the *Hellfire Prophecy.*

"The NRA is not in the business of predicting apocalypses,"

Michael McCloud, senior press secretary, said. "However, we do applaud any efforts to create a bulwark against tyrannical governmental overreach, and we support the recent surge in purchases of firearms for such purposes. We will never rest against this constant threat. To reiterate, we had nothing to do with *The Book of Strobe*."

There has been a 250% spike in the sales of personal protection firearms. While some of this may be explained by *The Book of Strobe*, the NRA's research analytics department has determined the majority of this uptick is the result of increasing American recognition of the inalienable right of citizens to own guns to protect themselves from all potential threats—a position continuously upheld by the Supreme Court of the United States. "We will continue to provide support to these individuals, up to and including the moment when all firearms are pried from our cold, deceased fingers," McCloud said.

*About the NRA:* While widely recognized today as a major political force and as America's foremost defender of Second Amendment rights, the NRA has, since its inception, been the premier firearms education organization in the world. But our successes would not be possible without the tireless efforts and countless hours of service our nearly five million members have given to champion Second Amendment rights and support NRA programs. As former Clinton spokesman George Stephanopoulos said, "Let me make one small vote for the NRA. They're good citizens. They call their congressmen. They write. They vote. They contribute. And they get what they want over time."\*

---

\* https://home.nra.org/about-the-nra/

**From: Ruby Witherspoon <ruby.witherspoon@aol.com>**
**To: Strobe Witherspoon <swither@wthrspnllc.com>**
**SUBJECT: re: re: Missing You**

Hi Strobe,

Your electronic mail made me cry. Thinking about Wheeler's memory getting attacked like this made me cry. Thinking about you thinking about this made me cry. I recognize that our family hasn't been perfect, but we don't deserve this. Even your father, who Lord knows deserves a lot of what has been handed to him, doesn't deserve this. I support whatever you think is best for you and for the family. If that includes contacting Richard, then so be it. If you do speak to him, send him my regards.

Always,
Ruby

# ICE raids Witherspoon house over immigrant sex-trafficking charges

NorthernMaineOnline.com

Shortly after 5:00 on Sunday morning, officials from the Immigration and Customs Enforcement (ICE) agency raided the home of Ruby Witherspoon. The purpose of the raid was to investigate multiple claims of an immigrant sex-trafficking ring being run out of the attic. No such sex-trafficking was found, but ICE officials reported that they would continue to monitor the situation. ICE maintains jurisdiction over such issues in Furstable Manor because the entire state of Maine is located within 100 air miles from the Canadian border.

# Health Officials Investigate Uncertified Abortion Clinic

TheMaineHerald.com

Local health department officials were called to the Furstable Manor home of Ruby Witherspoon after numerous tips came in through the town hotline about a satanic tattoo parlor acting without a license. No evidence of devil-worshipping tattoos was found. "We have a zero-tolerance policy on businesses operating without a license," said John Maxwell, deputy chief of the Health Department.

The Witherspoon residence could not be reached for comment.

# SWAT Engages in Tense Standoff

NewEnglandToday.com

State police have determined that reports of a hostage situation at the home of Ruby Witherspoon were false. A group of internet pranksters allegedly convinced the police to stake out the elderly woman's home. The police brought the SWAT team with them. An apparently agitated man shouted profanity at the SWAT team members when they arrived, prompting them to shoot out his windows. A full investigation was conducted, and no hostages were found. No charges were filed, and the Maine State Police extended their apologies to Witherspoon for the misunderstanding.

# Local Officials React
# to Swath of "Swatting"

TheNorthernMaineTribune.com

Bureaucratic silos are apparently to blame after a spate of prank calls directed at part-time Furstable resident Strobe Witherspoon shook this normally sleepy hamlet. Witherspoon, whose mother Ruby owns a house in Furstable Manor, has been the subject of intense media speculation in recent weeks over the sale of his most recent book, *FLO-TUS: a memoir*. Upon investigating the incidents, the local sheriff's department announced that Mr. Witherspoon has been the victim of "acute swatting." Swatting has become popular in recent years, defined as "the action or practice of making a prank call to emergency services in an attempt to bring about the dispatch of a large number of armed police officers to a particular address."

The mayor of Furstable Manor called for the creation of a committee to study approaches to "disrupt bureaucratic silos so the people of Furstable can receive efficient and fair treatment from all levels of government."

"You just can't trust anybody these days," Felicia Von Hausen, 83, told the *Northern Maine Tribune*. "Do we need a committee to tell us that?" she asked.

"I'm getting real tired of waking up to some new rigmarole over at the Witherspoon house. From what I can tell, it all smells a little fishy to me, so I'm still gonna sleep with my pistol, if any of them folks are listenin'," said Brad Munson, 48.

For now, local officials have pledged to increase surveillance capabilities and direct additional resources to securing the area around the Witherspoon home.

# 51

# The Toothpaste Is Out of the Tube

## By Derek Blum

The New Patriot

I was privy to the behavior. During my stint in the previous administration, I saw what was happening. If I'm being honest, I enabled it. For political advantage? Yes. These theories that were bubbling up from the dark underbelly of the internet and taking hold of the imaginations of highly persuadable voters were useful in our efforts to undermine our opponents. As communications director, I felt like I had no choice but to embrace this approach.

When we came across a fringe theory on the internet about one of our most outspoken political opponents' connection to an offshore bank that had recently been exposed as a money-laundering destination for heroin smugglers, we had no problem furthering the narrative that this politician was, by association, a ruthless killer and a drug dealer. Never mind that the connection to the offshore bank turned out to be false (or that others in our administration actually had parked a lot of their money there). It was okay, I told myself, because this person was also responsible for undermining many of our administration's key legislative initiatives.

The hesitant members of the administration were easy to spot. Occasionally verbalizing their concern about the conspiracy theory approach (CTA) after a drink or two. This usually led to their removal via any number of delegitimization methods.

That's how it went for me. First came the email leaks that revealed the not-very-well-kept secret of my romantic life. Then came the swarms of pearl-clutching pitchfork wielders. Then came the announcement, delivered to me and the rest of the country via Tweet, that proclaimed my interest in spending more time with my family.

I didn't want to spend more time with my family. My marriage had been effectively over for almost a decade. My kids were in college. They were so embarrassed by my job that they used their mother's maiden name.

But here we are, and a few years have passed. My boyfriend and I live together. I have found a new home at this upstart magazine and newsletter. The process of reconciliation has begun. I wouldn't necessarily call it stress free, however. As I write this, my stock portfolio has lost half its value, thanks in large part to *The Book of Strobe: the fifth cycle of the Hellfire Prophecy.*

This "Book" provides an answer to the question, "Were these conspiracy theories getting too dumb to be effective?" The answer is a resounding NO.

Which is why I now find myself committed to destroying the scourge that I helped create. Baseless conspiracies are no longer a somewhat harmless tool in an "all's fair in love and war" political environment. They are the thing that broke my unwavering commitment to the party that used to be about small government and free markets, the party I have spent my entire life supporting.

In the coming months, I am going to go deeper. I will do my best to lay out the sources and methods of political malfeasance that has propelled us to the precipice of destruction. I am going to tell stories that will paint me in an unflattering light. I am going to name names. I am going to reveal the cynical role that all of us from the previous administration played in creating the conspiracy theory–dominated marketplace of bad ideas that we now find ourselves consumed by.

To be clear, the left will not be immune from my wrath. Just as Orwell's *1984* is more about totalitarianism than communism, my efforts here will be about exposing the awfulness of all that I have seen, regardless of the political ideology attached to it. Remember the widespread reporting on a secret abortion clinic owned and operated by wealthy conservatives? Yeah, that was false, spread by our rivals for political gain. And I have proof.

It is my hope that this will help neutralize this force in our society and build a populace that is able to identify and ignore the rampant misinformation campaigns thrust upon us in the past, present (I'm looking at you, deepfake videos), and will be thrust upon us in the future, in ways we cannot yet fathom.

It is the least I can do to repay my debt. And maybe try and put the toothpaste back in the tube.

*Derek Blum is a former White House communications director and author of the upcoming book, "The Last Honest Man in the Room."*

# EXCLUSIVE: Strobe and Richard Witherspoon Uncut

bookjacketquotes.com

**Editor's Note:** Sitting on two neglected Adirondack chairs set amongst overgrown shrubs in Ruby's Maine house backyard, Strobe and Richard Witherspoon reunited for the first time in over twenty years. They demonstrated an ambivalent stiffness toward each other. The camera could see but not hear their discussion. When they came inside, they took their seats in two frayed, oversized armchairs in the living room. The following is a transcript of the conversation that followed. It was livestreamed via YouTube and Amber Witherspoon's web site.

**SW:** We're gonna get this going and try to keep it civilized, right Pop.

**RW:** Sure.

**SW:** Sure you're OK with this?

**RW:** Not sure. How do I know this won't backfire like the last one of these things I did?

**SW:** We don't know. We just wanna see if the truth will, ah, set us free.

**RW:** That's bullshit.

**SW:** Everybody has taken this story and turned it into whatever they want. It's our turn to take it back.

**RW:** You believe the crap that comes out of your mouth?

**SW:** You got a better idea?

**RW:** Track down these punks and teach 'em a lesson.

**SW:** That's a lot of lessons.

**RW:** The one's that hacked my social security checks and unenrolled me from Medicare Part D, let's start with them.

**SW:** So we both have been the victims of some pretty dumb shit.

**RW:** Yes.

**SW:** And we both want to clear our names.

**RW:** I'd like to clear my name. Who the hell knows what you're up to.

**SW:** Same as you Pop. This is all I can think of, believe me, if there was another way...

**RW:** Great.

**SW:** Would now be a bad time to address the camera? [Turning to camera] Does this look like a father son combo that's about to coordinate the Hellfire Prophecy?

**RW:** Enough of that.

**SW:** Of what?

**RW:** That smirk. I'll tell you what, people watching this are probably saying to themselves, 'yeah, you condescending prick, we totally think you would pull that shit.'

**SW:** You seem like you may be one of them.

**RW:** All I know is what I see with my own two eyes. To be honest, it's a little too wacky for me. It's a distraction.

**SW:** OK.

**RW:** The freeloaders screwing everything up and getting support from the bankers and the limousine liberals. They're bussing 'em in here by the thousands to sway our elections. After they brainwash them all into voting for other limp wristed socialists who knows what's gonna happen to this country. No one wants to talk about that.

**SW:** Seems like a lot of people are talking about that.

**RW:** Not enough people.

**SW:** What about your Medicare?

**RW:** What about it?

**SW:** Are the socialists coming for that?

**RW:** They better not.

**SW:** So, that handout can't be touched.

**RW:** Do you even pay attention to what's happening in Venezuela?

**SW:** I don't.

**RW:** When I was teaching those kids. I saw it coming. They were so naïve.

**SW:** You don't think that's also a little condescending?

**RW:** It's the truth. I'm not hiding behind some devil may care attitude. I'm looking you in the eye like a man.

**SW:** I think we've broken the ice. So that's good.

**RW:** Changing the subject are we?

**SW:** Trying to keep us on track. But we can talk about whatever you want. As long as it helps us make our case that we AREN'T IN ANY WAY CONNECTED TO THE HELLFIRE PROPHECY.

**RW:** I guess that's your big plan? Get us to bicker on camera so people stop pranking us?

**SW:** If that's what it takes.

**RW:** I'm not optimistic.

**SW:** Well maybe we make some money off the ads.

**RW:** YouTube kicked off my favorite guy.

**SW:** So you don't want any of that revenue?

**RW:** How much we talkin about? I bet they snatch it from us when they find out I'm involved.

**SW:** You think that YouTube is gonna not pay us ad revenue because Richard Witherspoon is involved?

**RW:** Well, they kicked me off too. I like to comment on videos. Set people straight.

**SW:** What kind of comments?

**RW:** Just comments. About the lies of the mainstream media and their decades long campaign to numb us into some superficial reality show stupor that consolidates all the money in their hands and props up their misguided ideologies. The libs only care about looking like they care and then mocking us from their private fuel guzzling jets, with their personal trainers and plastic surgeons. That's why they need to be stopped.

**SW:** Stopped from what?

**RW:** The destruction of America. Anybody that doesn't see that isn't paying attention.

**SW:** You should have your own show.

**RW:** I'm workin on it.

**SW:** Maybe we should go back to your last few weeks. How has it been with all of this going on?

**RW:** My inbox is full of people telling me to kill myself. My Facebook got hacked and someone started posting stuff about secret clues to this Shitfire Prophecy thing and now I can't even go online anymore to get my news or comment on any videos. All of Reddit is basically convinced I'm Satan. It sucks.

**SW:** You miss those people.

**RW:** I can barely walk up and down the stairs. I don't drink anymore. I hate every movie that comes out. But I had that community. It's not much. I know. But it's somethin'.

**SW:** On the bright side, this did bring us back together.

**RW:** Look how great that's going.

**SW:** You think we're going to hang out after this?

**RW:** I don't know, do you, wise ass?

**SW:** I guess it's hard to say. This wasn't just about clearing our names. So maybe all isn't lost.

**RW:** That felt like an act.

**SW:** Can't you just accept that I wanted to see you just a little? Not a lot, don't worry. But you're my effin father.

**RW:** I'm still struggling with what it is that you do. But yeah, I guess one thing that this has done is, you know, reconnect us. Which...

**SW:** Yeah.

**RW:** A lot's happened.

**SW:** Yeah.

**RW:** It's not always easy.

**SW:** Things add up. Over time...

**RW:** I know I screwed up.

**SW:** You do?

**RW:** Your mother wasn't exactly a saint you know.

**SW:** So you made up an entirely false life?

**RW:** She would just guilt me all day and night. About the money, about my drinking. About parenting. She loved to pay for everything.

**SW:** She loved that?

**RW:** Yes. That's how she controlled me. I had plans.

**SW:** Baseball?

**RW:** Among other things.

**SW:** What other things?

**RW:** Business ideas.

**SW:** You never talked about business ideas.

**RW:** YOU NEVER ASKED!

**SW:** I WAS A KID!

**RW:** Whatever, they didn't happen. I had some bad luck in the market. A few things didn't really pan out. That made your mother happy.

**SW:** I doubt that.

**RW:** You would.

**SW:** I do.

**RW:** I was embarrassed.

**SW:** So you made up an entirely false life?

**RW:** You didn't understand then. And you don't now. I was trapped. I was out of options. Your mother was ready to put me out to pasture.

**SW:** You crushed your baseball career against the dash-board after you ran the car into a telephone pole. While drinking.

**RW:** Whatever it was, that ending hit me hard. Nobody seemed to understand that.

**SW:** I feel like a lot of people understood it. You just didn't accept it.

**RW:** I dealt with it.

**SW:** So you made up an entirely false life? And watched your son who idolized you do everything he could to imitate your false life?

**RW:** That wasn't the plan.

**SW:** It was for me.

**RW:** You ever hear of free will? Stop playing the victim.

**SW:** What about Wheeler?

**RW:** What about him?

**SW:** You think he was a victim?

[Pause]

**Editor's Note:** Richard walked out of the room when this question was asked. Strobe followed. About thirty minutes later, they returned and sat down.

**SW:** Where were we?

**RW:** You were attacking me for my bad life decisions.

**SW:** Right. How about my life decisions? You think I'm part of the deep state global elite because of my earlier career? Or do you think I'm a Hollywood elite that wants to lecture middle America about climate change while I fly around in my private jet?

**RW:** Can't it be both?

**SW:** Let's take it one at a time. You don't trust the government. Neither do I. I worked there. I've told you this before, but for the listeners—all I did was write reports about social movements in other countries and how they may affect US national interests. It was occasionally interesting, mostly tedious work, using lots of local news outlets and translators to basically tell everyone what they already know: the kids are restless, particularly in societies that limit their recreation.

**RW:** And?

**SW:** And that was it.

**RW:** That's what you say.

**SW:** Sometimes I listened to rap artists' protest songs in autocratic countries. Then I assessed their threat level to political stability. It was ...underwhelming. I wrote hundred page papers about what would happen if those factions rise up and topple the sitting government.

**RW:** You don't ever think about what those papers were used for?

**SW:** I can count on one hand the number of people that skimmed them. It's possible nobody ever read any of them in their entirety. By the end of my time there I would slip in a sentence about aliens just to see if anybody caught it. A lot of us did that. You know how many times someone caught it?

**RW:** None?

**SW:** Once, when someone did a CTRL-F for "Illegal Alien". They thought it was hilarious.

**RW:** That's what they want you to believe, all the while they're creating their manipulation machines.

**SW:** Most people I worked with couldn't even manipulate a lunch order. I'm curious, when did you develop so much confidence in the ingenuity of the human race?

**RW:** It's all just right there. Create the impression of self-determination, aka DEMOCRACY, turn everyone's brains to mush with a barrage of lifestyle programming, then turn around and tell them that the government is the answer to all of that stuff that is out of reach. Then you consolidate power and, powie!, control the masses. You get to maintain your wealth and power. And you can snuggle up each night with a warm blanket of sanctimony and a nice hot cup of condescension while the rest of the country freezes in the wilderness of complacency.

**SW:** You seem to be quite certain about this.

**RW:** Look, do I think you're behind this global charade to consolidate power? No. Do I think you have been a pawn in that game? Yes.

**SW:** Well that's certainly not gonna put a stop to the hate mail.

**RW:** It's the truth.

**SW:** You think the NRA is behind the Hellfire Prophecy?

**RW:** I think it might actually be the gun control nuts. Maybe they figure they can kill two birds with one stone. Destroy the gun lobby and distract the masses while everyone is stocking up on end of days kits. Then they sweep in and pretend to save the world.

**SW:** My response to that will always be: humans—sooooo not capable of that kind of coordination.

**RW:** You just haven't done the research.

**SW:** I suspect that's true. I try not to go on the Internet if I don't have to.

**RW:** Unless you wanna make fun of it.

**SW:** Right. Can't you take a break from it?

**RW:** I'm an outcast in the real world. Not even the super-market is safe anymore. You know what kee noah is?

**SW:** Quinoa?

**RW:** Of course you know what that is.

**SW:** You think you can take a break from the Internet?

**RW:** When you can laugh at those people that don't get it it feels like I'm not going crazy. Seeing people we loathe get so worked up about it makes it all worth it.

**SW:** You think if you stopped hanging out on the Internet you would go back to the booze?

**RW:** Maybe.

**SW:** Maybe?

**RW:** I don't wanna think about it. Too many bad memories.

**SW:** Baseball?

**RW:** I still think about Wheeler on the stretcher. Asking me what happened. I had one job. Secure the saddle. I still remember it. Trying to fasten it with one hand while I snuck a tug from the flask. Watching him hop on and take off, knowing that it wasn't fastened. I remember shrugging. Then watching it slide off, in slow motion, bringing Wheelie down on his neck. It's frozen in time. The whole thing. I knew you knew.

**SW:** I couldn't even think straight at the hospital.

**RW:** I shouldn't have asked you to take the heat.

SW: You think?

RW: I knew your mother would cut me off completely if I admitted it. Which, well, she did anyway, and you abandoned me.

SW: Be honest, he was your favorite.

RW: For fuck's sake.

SW: I was obsessed with becoming a spy.

RW: You asked a lot of questions.

SW: You answered them all.

RW: Most of them were wrong. I didn't know shit about spying.

SW: Even though the WASP tradition in the CIA goes back to the beginning?

RW: You think I knew about that? That was your mother's side. My side were farmers. Poor. Scottish catholic. The Biddlestons were the WASPs. I'm sure they had some Freemasons in there also. To anyone that's listening—

SW: Did you come all the way here to basically hang me and mom out to dry?

RW: I'm just saying that the Witherspoon heritage has been totally mischaracterized and I'm here to set that record straight.

SW: And me? You still think I may be pulling some secret levers off in the shadows?

**RW:** I'm not commenting on that because I don't know you.

**SW:** You're my father.

**RW:** Your life decisions are not mine.

**SW:** I joined the CIA to impress you!

**RW:** I'm sorry you felt the need to do that.

**SW:** I tried to cover up Wheeler's death to protect you!

**RW:** I know.

**SW:** I got fired because of it!

**RW:** I know.

**SW:** And you still think I'm part of some elite globalist plot against America?

**RW:** I don't even know if you know if you are.

**SW:** Now I'm a Manchurian Deep Stater?

**RW:** Not everybody is at the meeting where they decide to use minorities as weapons of false democracy.

**SW:** It sounds like you're still listening to the Daily Dose a lot.

**RW:** Every day.

**SW:** Even though their listeners have turned on you?

**RW:** I can't worry about that. What would I do if I just cut that off?

**SW:** I'm still here.

**RW:** Are you?

**SW:** I don't know.

**RW:** Exactly.

**SW:** Twenty years pop.

**RW:** That's a long time. People change.

**SW:** You're still my father.

**RW:** I know.

**SW:** And?

**RW:** And I'm sorry that this has all gotten so out of hand.

**SW:** I'm sorry too.

**RW:** My knee is killin me in this chair.

**SW:** Is that your way of asking if we can be done?

**RW:** I don't know how much more I have left in the tank.

**SW:** We can be done.

**RW:** Thanks.

*Richard slowly took off his headphones, put his jacket on, took out some pills, walked to the sink in the kitchen, swallowed the pills with some water cupped in his hands, and stared at his son, leaning on the sink.*

*"Next time, without the microphones," Richard said.*

*Strobe gave a minimal nod. Richard limped out the door, slower than when he arrived.*

# RICHARD WITHERSPOON SHOT DEAD

Central News Network

An unnamed gunman was arrested today for the shooting of Richard Witherspoon. Witherspoon was exiting the house owned by his ex-wife, Ruby. Motives for the murder have not been identified, but authorities stated they are not ruling out a possible link to an apocalyptic theory gaining popularity within certain online communities. This theory includes provocative speculation about Richard and his son Strobe Witherspoon's role in controlling the levers of government.

This is a breaking news story and will be updated.

# MITCH WITHERSPOON VLOG UPDATE 2471

---

Transcript

---

**MW:** Hi everybody. Obviously this update comes to you under difficult circumstances. I was debating whether or not to even turn the camera on. But I feel like you all, my audience, are the only ones who really can appreciate my trauma in this moment, and I want to be with you all, together, as I process it.

[WAITER'S ARM APPEARS FROM OFF CAMERA WITH TEA]

Yo! I said no more tea! C'mon.

I'm sitting here in Bangladesh, trying to be all Zen, all while everything is crumbling back home. I cancelled my meeting with the Child Street Vendors Alliance today because I couldn't focus. It doesn't feel like the right time.

He was my grandpa. And someone shot him dead.

It's so confusing. After I did that vlog a few weeks back lots of people were accusing me of trying to sell out my family.

I just wanted to tell people that they should think for themselves. Like me.

Next thing I knew there was gonna be some big manifesto about my dad and his dad and their "plans" to control the world.

I swear, I have nothin' to do with that stuff. I read things with my own eyes. My own eyes told me that my family might not be exactly what I thought growing up.

Now I have people tweeting at me with all this crazy stuff about me being next. I'm not next! I have nothing to do with any of this!

Sorry, I shouldn't be yelling.

But it's hard. I'm walkin' down this street, looking over my shoulder and worrying that someone is going to jump out of a rickshaw and just take me out. That's ridiculous. THIS is ridiculous. My grandpa is dead.

So, this may be my last vlog for a little while. I'm not gonna say more than that. But to those that believe in me, we will meet again. Soon, I hope.

# 55

**FROM: Jotham ‹QUINTASMCONTRA1@substack.com›**
**To: OldFedupGroup**
**Subject: staying focused**

Hola Contra Comrades (ALLIES!). Lot's happening over here at QC HQ. First off, we (DEFINITELY) did not kill Richard Witherspoon. Please make sure you reiterate that to all those that make that kind of (OUTLANDISH) claim. We. Do. Not. Condone (ENDORSE). Acts. Of. Violence (EVER).

While it seems that this patriot may have had a different target in mind (STROBE), the mission, in this person's mind, must not be considered a failure (ALTHOUGH ANY MISSION THAT INVOLVES MURDER IS NOT SOMETHING THAT WE CONDONE).

We can only imagine the chaos in the Illuminati HQ right now (THEY SCARED). While we mourn the loss of any human life, this is a clear signal that the people of this great country will not stand by and let their country be run by a shadowy cabal (GLOBALISTS). To all those that are still down with the Fed Up! group, be forewarned: they are not to be trusted. Their silence in the last week has been deafening. This tells me that they are not the patriots we once thought they were.

Their commitment to the revolution appears to be faltering, and if I were you, I would unsubscribe to their email.

Which is all to say, we Contras must remain vigilant (READY TO FIGHT). The followers of the Hellfire Prophecy may have lost a leader, but they are not out of resources by any stretch (MONEY!). They will continue to try and compromise and coerce your former friends over at Fed Up! And it is our responsibility to protect ourselves from their mind control and subjugation (SLAVERY). By. Whatever. Means. Necessary (NOT VIOLENCE).

Rise Up,
QC Jotham

# 56

**From: Ruby Witherspoon <ruby.witherspoon@aol.com>**
**To: Strobe Witherspoon <swither@wthrspnllc.com>**
**SUBJECT: re: Missing You**

Strobe,

I tried calling to no avail. Please tell me you're OK.

This is all so hard to comprehend. What is happening? I'm struck by just how much anger there is in this world that has no useful outlet.

Richard didn't deserve to die in such an undignified manner. I'm sorry, but when a man dies at the hands of a stranger over claims that are obviously untrue, there is something wrong with us. Deeply wrong. Why are they so willing to accept this nonsense? I can't even understand how it all came to this.

We now have four security guards at the senior center. There has been a motion from our council to expel me from my residence. The board director has told people that he thinks I am connected to the "situation." Just today a person pretending to be a nurse was caught stealing computer hard drives from the computer center. I eat by myself. There is only one employee here that will talk to me.

Please don't try to be a hero Strobelight. Let's persevere the way the Witherspoon's have always persevered – through hard work and kindness of spirit.

OK?

I love you.

Always,
Ruby

**From: Mail Delivery System**
**To: ruby.witherspoon@aol.com**
**X-Failed-Recipients: swither@wthrspnllc.com**
**Subject: re: Missing You**

Mail delivery failed: returning message to sender
Message-Id:

This message was created automatically by mail delivery software.

Amessagethatyousentcouldnotbedeliveredtooneormoreofits recipients. This is a permanent error. The following address(es) failed:

swither@wthrspnllc.com

No Such User

# Mitch Witherspoon Vlog Update 2472

---

Transcript

---

**MW:** I know. I said I was taking some time off. I couldn't do it. This community and this message is too important to me. You all are my family through thick and thin. And it's important that I don't close up during the thin. I must let radical transparency guide me.

Perseverance is critical. For all of us. I'm still a work in progress. My progress IS work. I don't avert my eyes to the abyss. I recognize the abyss for what it is. That's some Nietzsche:

[Looks down on a piece of paper]

"And if thou gaze long into an abyss, the abyss will also gaze into thee."

I'm thinking about a forearm tattoo with that in Sanskrit. What do you all think? Lemme know in the comments. My spiritual advisor here in Laurel Canyon

– Brother Sidney – he laid that knowledge on me. And I saw it, right in front of my face, the truth I have been looking all over the world for, here in the transcendent hills of California. Strength through meditation. Power through presence. Victory through submission.

The press likes to call this practice militant Buddhism, but I know better. At its core, it's just some deep spiritual and physical exercise for the soul. And let me tell you I was out of shape. A lot of us are.

I thought that #ZENLIFE was all about going everywhere, doing everything, and displaying it all to the world. How wrong I was. It's about appreciating what's around you. Interrogating your soul with all of your might. But also, communing with technology. Which is so important. The communication networks that drive human connection must be used for good. The people here at the Laurel Canyon Buddhist Coalition recognize that. Already I have come up with a few aggressive mindfulness app ideas that some really important people at the LCBC seem really interested in.

There is one really really important person here. Sister Claudia. Come in here.

[A young woman enters the frame]

Claudia, say something to the camera.

[Sister Claudia grins, combines her hands into a prayer position, bows her head, looks up, and shuts her eyes]

C'mon, say hello.

[Sister Claudia opens her eyes and makes eye contact with Mitch. She grins again and then closes her eyes again]

Ok it's OK.

[Sister Claudia stands up and exits the frame]

You may recognize her, she's an actress. She used to be on *Fully Loaded: Mykonos*. I watched that show so much. I always felt a connection with Claudia. And now, and now... enough of that, no need to get the paparazzi out here disrupting our tranquility.

So much love in the air. My body is not used to it. The exhaustion is part of the initiation, Brother Sydney told me. I get it, but man, was I weak. I tell you what, when you have a partner like sister Claudia, you find the strength.

Anyway, look, I'm not trying to pretend that the world isn't full of darkness. A lot of people, they looked into the abyss, the abyss looked back at them, and the next thing you know, they were the abyss. And I know some of y'all gonna laugh at me in the comments for saying this, but I really do think there is a way out, through the aggressive accommodation of all living things in our kinosphere, including our own selves and the technology that is the extension of our self. Let those electromagnetic vibrations cascade through-out your body, your phones, your community and let that energy transport the organic nature of human connection. It's not complicated. But it's going to take work.

It's not gonna bring my grandpa back. Not in his physical form. But I can use that sadness to open up new networks of discovery within myself, which will open me up to others and close me off to the negativity that modern society has brought upon us, with the bureaucrats, the plutocrats, and the kleptocrats, all the crats that have been nibbling away at our essences over time, creating a vicious circle of corruption, deception, and despair. These were the things that brought down my grandpa and now threaten my father.

I am committed to breaking that chain. Only love in the comments section please.

# 59

# Good-bye

## by Strobe Witherspoon

HellisOtherPeoplesBlogs.com

Those of you following this deeply disappointing chapter in human history are probably wondering what happened to me after my father was killed. I ran. Out the back door, into the wooded area behind my house, through some other properties, onto the road, and then, finally, to the police station. I sprained my ankle.

The police had questions. One of the policemen knew me. He was a believer in the Hellfire Prophecy, or at least was interested in telling me everything about it that he knew. After he finished talking about things like presidential bloodlines—they are all related!—and secret money-printing schemes that have kept these bloodlines richer than the rest of the world, he looked at me. Just stared right at me. A policeman, paid by the city to protect citizens, was convinced that the government was a sham. It's a strange feeling when a law-enforcement officer outdoes you on your governmental skepticism.

**OOF**

As I walked out of the station, I had an epiphany.

Sometimes the most difficult thing to do is nothing.

I was consistently wrong about my ability to fix this.

I'm the biggest idiot of them all.

I should stop.

# 60

**Editor's Note:** *Strobe contacted me. He told me that he didn't think he could continue our project, but that I should take it forward if I wished.*

*I found it energizing—as if Strobe's weakness was filling me with resolve. My participation in this endeavor was no longer secondary. It was now my responsibility to collect and preserve the details of this event for posterity. I realized that this truth war would be fought on many fronts. This compendium would be one of those fronts.*

*Meanwhile, fallout from the Online Outrage Fiesta continued:*

## DOW DROPS ON HELLFIRE PROPHECY FEARS

Markets continue downward slide as online conspiracy theory transitions to real-world conflict, with no resolution in sight.

## STROBE WITHERSPOON'S
## WHEREABOUTS REMAIN A MYSTERY

Authorities would like to talk to the son of slain spy Richard Witherspoon. First, they'll need to find him.

## GLOBAL MARKETS IN TAILSPIN

Downgraded US economy sparks selloff as analysts see global risk of contagion.

## VOLATILITY DOOM LOOP HAS
## HEDGE FUNDS CRYING FOUL

Big players complain about market manipulation and beg for bailouts.

## GOLD PRICES SPIKE

Currency uncertainty breathes new life into gold-bug investment philosophy.

## ATTACKS ON GOLD RESERVES SPIKE

Armed criminals create jitters for owners of large gold holdings; cottage industry for gold security services expands.

## DOOMSDAY SPELLS PAYDAY

Canned goods, camping equipment, face masks, and firearms sales remain strong as belief in Hellfire Prophecy picks up steam.

# 61

# Five Questions About The Quintasm, Answered

Time Magazine

### 1. What's the difference between the Quintasm, the Hellfire Prophecy, and *The Book of Strobe*?

Many people just learning about this topic are confused by these various references. Here's a quick metaphorical overview:

The Hellfire Prophecy is the castle on the hill, the Quintasm is the moat separating the Hellfire architects from the castle, and *The Book of Strobe* is the vehicle that crosses the moat to get into the castle.

In other words, the Hellfire Prophecy is the endgame—the final destination of a manmade end-times scenario that a small but powerful group of people is trying to orchestrate.

The Quintasm is the fifth and final cycle (the other four have been completed) of the Prophecy (i.e., the castle). Seen another way, completion of the Quintasm cycle is the final obstacle to cross (i.e., the moat) to reach the castle.

*The Book of Strobe* is the text that lays out the key participants in the Quintasm. These participants, led by Strobe Witherspoon, are the driving forces (i.e., vehicle) that are tasked with completing the Quintasm (crossing the moat) in order to get to the castle on the hill (prophecy) and bask in its riches.

## 2. Why am I just hearing of this theory?

This theory has only recently made it out of the fringe and into the mainstream. The author of this manifesto—A. Nona Mouse (ANM)—remains a mystery. Efforts to follow his internet tracks have been mostly unsuccessful, but some clues suggest that ANM is well connected to key figures of the Azerbaijani dark web and is utilizing innovative message distribution tools to spread his message while deploying complex camouflaging mechanisms to remain anonymous. Some of the connections seem to go back further. One influencer by the name of Liberty Lisa has recently been deplatformed due to suspected links with the Azerbaijani dark web. This popular right-wing YouTube star was allegedly paid to launch the boycott campaign of Witherspoon's book *FLOTUS: a memoir*. By paying influencers on the internet to demonstrate extreme outrage for this forthcoming book, the theory goes, the stage was set for the proliferation of the Hellfire Prophecy manifesto.

### 3. Was Richard Witherspoon really killed because of his role in this theory?

Richard Witherspoon's purported role in the Hellfire Prophecy remains a possible motive for his murder that authorities are investigating. The prophecy presents Richard, father of Strobe, as a crucial component of this far-reaching theory.

### 4. Is Strobe Witherspoon behind all of this?

Originally, there were rumors that Strobe had cooked up this whole story as a publicity stunt for his new book. After the cancellation of his book and the death of his father, support for that theory declined. At this time, it's impossible to rule out another theory that this was all his idea until it spiraled out of control. Strobe's history of misdirection and false claims about his life make it difficult to reach firm conclusions about his role in this story.

### 5. Should I stock up on end-of-days items, including guns and ammo?

In this age of uncertainty and instability, experts suggest it's always a good idea to have a "go bag" ready.

# 62

# Mitch Witherspoon
# Vlog Update 2473

---

Transcript

---

**MW:** So this is just a quick update to let you know that I'm no longer at the LCBC. Claudia dumped me for Sydney. First she was talking about the freedom of polyamorous exploration and I was like, 'OK.' And now she wants to focus on 'solidifying the ties that bind her to one human.'

What?

That Tai Kwan Yoga class wasn't even on the schedule, which was my first clue. When I caught them doing sex things she just started talking down to me, like I couldn't understand their "connection." Like I was an idiot. Making up excuses to excuse her own failings.

I'm sick of everybody telling stories that make them feel better about themselves at my expense. My dad did that. This feels like that all over again.

When my mom kicked my dad out of the house, she told me to forget about him. But I didn't. I wanted him to love me. So I kept his secret about what happened after he got fired. Then I had to watch as he became a famous writer, telling everybody that the family came apart because he was too focused on his writing. Another BS story.

He didn't leave us to focus on his writing. My mom kicked him out. Money wasn't the issue. She kicked him out because he was a failure of a human being. He was a violent alcoholic that couldn't face up to his own failure and I'm sick of pretending otherwise. I'm sick of him pretending otherwise. Maybe if I told *the New Yorker* that we wouldn't be in this mess.

The LCBC is just as phony. Before Claudia dumped me she suggested we do some cross-promotional episodes about our awakening with Brother Sydney, who was launching the LCBC's new online meditation portal and movie studio. I was like, 'sure.' Then, after I find out Sydney has sent me into the cuck zone, he asks me if I could still promote the LCBC on my vlog. Like I'm going to just look the other way as he takes advantage of my generosity, of my social media presence, of my honor, to build his own brand. He's a fraud. She's a fraud. You both don't deserve exposure to my YouTube subscribers!

It's time for me to take back the narrative. Claudia, Sydney, my father, they're just attention starved narcissists, users, abusers. I'm sick of these desperate pleas for attention that aren't what they say they are.

# 63

# Chapter 6:
# I'm Sorry, My Son

I sometimes say that I "retired from the modeling industry in my mid-thirties." The truth is, I got fired from modeling. "Fired" is the term they use for models who have children and don't return to their pre-childbirth figure.

When I realized my career was over and my social responsibilities were taking a back seat to my child-rearing activities, I turned to eating. I was making up for lost time, I told myself. In reality, it was I who was lost. I had given up my life's dream and bore my husband a son only to be beset by postpartum depression and a partner who was growing less interested in me and more obsessed with politics by the day. Not coincidentally, this is when the invitations to the parties and galas started to dry up. Not for him, of course.

My child had no idea why I was so angry all the time. He didn't understand that everything I had worked for was yanked out from under me. I was empty inside. My son emptied me out, literally.

I always tried to cover for my bad behavior with presents and more presents. He seemed okay with that tradeoff. At least that's what I told myself.

I told people I was doing a lot of things: taking classes to get my high school diploma, starting my own modeling agency, learning to cook. In reality, I was hiding in my wing of the penthouse, watching *Zoolander* on DVD, and avoiding mirrors. I'm still embarrassed by my unsophisticated food choices during those days—Hawaiian pizzas, Twizzlers, disco fries. They were my companions back then. Today I know better.

During that era of pedestrian food consumption, seclusion, and self-loathing, the nannies knew what to do—keep me out of sight so I couldn't do any more damage to myself or others. They seemed happy not to have me around. I had the tendency to throw bowls of melted ice cream at them when they intruded on my solitude. My temper was out of control, and my targets were those closest to me.

But I could still hear the video games and the revelry from my gold-plated prison cell. My child and his surrogate parents partaking in endless Mortal Kombat tournaments while they ate whatever he wanted. My son owes those nannies a thank you. Not many children his age get that kind of freedom. I didn't have that freedom when I was his age.

For the record, I wasn't always mean to Liesa, Hilda, Filipa, and Charmaine. Right before Christmas, I would let them go into my closet and pick out one pair of shoes and one outfit. They were very appreciative. My connection to immigrants like them remained strong, despite my depression and elevated status. I didn't even get mad when I found out they were selling my clothes on eBay. People in their situation need to do what they have to do to get by.

Also, those clothes were grim reminders of a more confident time for me, when designers were eager to dress me and photographers were eager to show those outfits to the world.

My husband was not helpful. He mocked my weight to others. To my face.

"You're one Big Mac away from a heart attack yourself!" I once yelled at him.

"No, I'm not," he replied.

I was becoming my father before my eyes. His vice was drinking, mine was gorging. I had done everything in my power to escape that kind of violent selfishness, only to be blindsided by it in another country, under different circumstances, but with sadly similar results.

My violent temper began to dominate all of my interactions. My son, by the time he was eleven, was avoiding eye contact and sleeping in Hilda's apartment next door. What was once a more primitive, instinctual fear in his eyes was turning into a coldness that I recognized. I understood what was going through his head as he watched me succumb to violent, destructive behavior, because I knew what was going through my head when my father behaved that way.

All the video games and candy in the world wouldn't warm him up.

After a while, I started doing my own research about child psychology on the internet, where I learned that abuse at that age was shown to have a strong correlation with antisocial behavior later in life.

From there, I did more research. About a lot of things. My love for fine art blossomed. Then I took private painting classes. I started reading about nutrition and carbohydrates and cleanses. Then I hired the best trainers and chefs money could buy. They were in awe of my commitment.

I finally completed those online courses for my high school degree. Holding that diploma in my hand ignited something inside me that still burns with the heat of a thousand suns. Ten years later, I am the proud owner of a bachelor of arts degree in English and master's degrees in art history and sociology. As we speak, I am finishing up my applications for PhD programs, where I hope to focus on the semiotics of aesthetics. My American dream is alive and well.

I have come to accept that we all have our own paths and that mine included a dark period with some behavior unbecoming of a woman of my standing. But my path has made me stronger. It has made my bond with my son stronger.

I fear that he still bears the psychological scars of those early years, and they will someday manifest themselves through his own destructive behavior. I hope not. But the future isn't yet written. The healing process is a long and windy one. With myself. With my son.

We text with each other almost every week. He is the starting goalie for his lacrosse team at boarding school. He's got his eye on some great colleges, and I am confident that, with my support, he will be accepted wherever he applies. And they will be lucky to have him.

Maybe he'll read this and understand that I will always be sorry about those early years. I hope so.

**Editor's Note:** This FLOTUS chapter was allegedly leaked by VITAL Books. Internet speculation posited that this sample corroborated Mitch's story of his father's abuse and supported VITAL's decision to not publish the book.

# 64

# We Told You So

Bear Arms Blog (BAB)

Greetings patriots!!!!!!!

Some of you probably never thought you would find your-selves here at BAB, researching ways to stockpile weapons and ammunition in preparation for an imminent attack from our tyrannical government. Welcome. You won't regret it.

Remember, armed citizens don't regret. They reload.

First off, let's just state the obvious. The bubble has burst, and everyone is now learning what I have been telling my friends for decades: "trust is a four letter word. So is govern-ment." Our forefathers knew it, which is why they created such a clear-eyed, well-crafted, totally relevant in a modern context second amendment. Shout out to all my Heller peeps who always believed.

To my long-time readers, I say: aren't you glad you aren't trying to learn about this stuff for the first time? I know I am.

To the newbies: I'm here to help.

Let's get this out of the way – I have no cotton pickin clue about this Hellfire Prophecy thing. Seems kinda funny to me. I do enjoy watching these libs get all worked up by it. This prophecy may be real, it may be some elaborate troll op, but regardless, you need to be prepared, because there's a storm brewin, and the only people that gonna survive that storm are gonna be the ones with their heads on a swivel and their fingers on a trigger.

In my next post I will start to specifically lay out tips and tricks for optimizing your arsenal under a potential hellfire scenario, because hey, you have to admit, that may be what we're dealing with. Regardless, it's about freekin time to prepare the citizen army that our forefathers laid out for us.

So, keep reading for my updated buyer's guides. As always, clicking on the relevant firearm links below is what keeps me in business, and keeps my sponsors happy. Don't be shy people, I can't keep providing you the guidance against tyranny that you've come to expect without you clicking on those links!

# 65

# Charting Persuasionary Polemics:

## A Hellfire Prophecy Case Study

The Journal of Sociocultural Epidemiology (JoSE)

### Abstract:

**Introduction:** The rapid rise in interest and support for the Hellfire Prophecy—first on the fringes of the internet and now into mainstream discourse—offers the psychology community a unique opportunity to gain insight into the growing field of persuasive tactical manipulation. A better understanding of the dynamics of this case study can provide insights for future endeavors of persuasionary polemics.

**Methods:** Using word and phrase internet trend analysis and surveys, we identified flashpoints of virality. Word trend data collected included "Hellfire Prophecy," "Quintasm," "Strobe Witherspoon Conspiracy," and other such combinations.

**Results:** The first appearance of *The Book of Strobe* and its references to the Quintasm and the Hellfire Prophecy were not impactful—the book had fewer than fifty internet references the first month after its publication.

A large spike in social media attention occurred three weeks later. This activity was originally contained geographically to computers from one town in Azerbaijan. Over the next week, this activity spread to social media accounts throughout much of the United States. Within two months, it enjoyed widespread attention throughout Europe and Latin America as well.

Accordingly, awareness levels for this phenomenon, as indicated by survey respondents, indicate strong temporal and geographic correlation to the promotion of *The Book of Strobe* via an aggressive social media campaign originating in Azerbaijan.

It took approximately five days (95% CI [4.1-6.3]) of Hellfire Prophecy social media inundation before individuals transitioned from an awareness level of "do not know about" to "very aware." And their belief in the theory took approximately eleven days (95% CI [9.8-13.2]) to move from "inaccurate" to "accurate."

**Conclusion:** This study provides evidence that persistent persuasionary polemical tactics deployed by foreign actors can create decisive shifts in awareness and support for otherwise unknown social and cultural narratives.

Based on geographic genotyping, there is statistically significant evidence that the virality of the apocalyptic Hellfire Prophecy was driven by intense support from a single actor (aka "troll farm") in Azerbaijan. This genotyping does not allow for specific actor identification but suggests the firm formally known as Executive International Internet (EII) or one of its surrogates played a role.

EII was a so-called "troll farm" recently shut down for attempting to influence American political debates. It was headquartered in the same Azerbaijani town that originated the Hellfire Prophecy viral campaign. Efforts to stem these campaigns have been thwarted by the entities' easy dissolution and reformulation under different names, sometimes in different countries. Building an evidence base of these activities can help to galvanize support for more efficient and robust global monitoring mechanisms and enforcement policies.

# 66

**From: Ruby Witherspoon <ruby.witherspoon@aol.com>**
**To: Dan Manson <danthemanson@mansoninc.com>**
**SUBJECT: My Son**

Hello Dan,

This is Ruby Witherspoon, your client Strobe Witherspoon's mother. I am writing because I am trying to locate my son. His emails have bounced back and calling his phone takes me to his voicemail, but it will not let me leave a message.

I don't know what to do. He is sometimes hard to track down during the best of times. I am afraid that now is not the best of times for him or our family.

When he was first starting out as a writer, we would some-times talk about his anger issues and how he felt like writing helped him deal with his disappointment with the human race. Over time, he said that he thought he might be getting addicted to the provocation and the intrigue that his writing produced. I begged him to stop if it wasn't making him happy.

Now look what has happened. He is missing, his father is dead, and I can't even eat in the cafeteria at my living com-munity without people asking me to move out. When Mindy

Edelman invited a strange Eastern European man into the center and he made off with her iPad and family heirlooms, it was me she blamed! Next time maybe Mindy should think twice before believing a young stranger on the Internet that claims to love her.

I do know that Strobe thought highly of you, and that he still might have ambitions, or a desire to use this debacle to his professional advantage, so I thought perhaps you could reach him. If so, can you please let him know that I love him. If he is running out of money, I can help. I have not been many things to my son that I should have been—honest, strong, to name a few—but I have been able to provide him with financial security when necessary.

Hope all is well.

Ruby Witherspoon

# 67

# B/SENSITIVE_MEN

BLATHR – SOCIAL MEDIA'S
ANNOYING STEPCHILD

**u/brokenhe@rt** - college grad just moved 2 new town. None of the women will talk to me. I think Im too sensitive around them. Am I DOOMED?

> **PUA PRO** - UR not doomed. Its easy @brokenhe@rt. treat em like they got nothin to offer and they will b urs. Sensitivety is not ur friend

> **FEELINGSARE4FOOLZ** - Def don't let em see you catch feelingz. Neg em til they know u in control. I can teach u. First class is free!

> **PUA PRO** - @FEELINGSARE4FOOLZ you crazy. Neggin doesn't work no mo.

> **MITCHWITHERBLOGS** - I showed my last girlfriend feelingz. She trampled all over them. With my spiritual advisor.

**FEELINGSARE4FOOLZ** - @MITCHWITHERBLOGS you a damn fool. NEVER TRUST YO SPIRITUAL ADVISOR AROUND UR GIRL.

**MITCHWITHERBLOGS** – I don't wanna be treated like a doormat.

**brokenhe@rt** – Hi @MITCHWITHERBLOGS. It's so confusing. I know that when I try to be myself around women they no interested.

**PUA PRO** – Follow my instutctions and you wont feel sad never again

**MITCHWITHERBLOGS** – Where are your instructions?

**PUA PRO** - I'll send em 2 u. Im also available for coaching. SATISFACTIN GARANTEED

**brokenhe@rt** – im interested

**MITCHWITHERBLOGS** - Me too.

# 68

# Journal Entry #1

My immediate surroundings: sitting in a portable camping chair in an undisclosed location, pad and paper in hand, eating my fourth can of refried beans of the day. My mind: perpetually wandering. My spirit: deflated.

I have, on occasion, been able to procure a newspaper. The updates have not been encouraging. Somehow, I am responsible for the incredible success of the doomsday prep industry and the looming failure of pretty much every other facet of the economy. My father would be proud.

One might think that this sorry state of economic affairs would give me some pleasure/schadenfreude. It does.

As I sit here with my feet resting on a buckling milk crate, I find myself indifferent to the suffering of a society that is so easily duped.

Maybe the best way to conclude this chapter of the human race is to let it all burn to the ground. Maybe doing nothing is the something I have been looking for. Maybe that's what my role should be: the quiet hermit receding from view as the castle on the hill burns down. (I got my hands on that scintillating *Time* magazine article about me.)

There will be no Strobe 2.0. If that sounds melodramatic, then so be it. The all-powerful hand of Strobe Witherspoon will not participate in this final puppet show. I guess they'll have to see what happens without me and figure out how to claim it as part of the larger plan.

I still do suffer from fleeting moments of grandeur and fantasize about scholars generations from now coming upon this journal and marveling at the incredible wisdom and resolve I demonstrated in the face of an absolute breakdown of reason and reality. They will study Strobe Witherspoon's life. They will pore over my decisions to see how one man stood up to it all by not standing up at all, thus planting the seeds for humanity's rebirth.

I think it's time for that fifth can of beans. And maybe a drink.

# 69

**From: FEDUP2001@substack.com**
**To: FUPATRIOTS**
**Subject: Please Hear Me Out**

FED UP! EMAIL UPDATE 4333:

Hey everybody.

Fed Up! Steve here with your latest update. I know that it's been a little while since the last update and I'm sorry for that. I have to be honest with you all. It's been a rough few weeks.

I have been completely paralyzed by fear and sadness and the rapid decline of this newsletter. The UNSUBSCRIBE notifications are coming in by the hundreds. This newsletter was once my saving grace. Now it has turned into my darkest nemesis.

When I started this little blast email five years ago I wanted to focus on the things that made me mad. Not the things that made me sad. Not my crippling depression and social awkwardness.

At its peak I had 124,000 subscribers. I was partnering with some great companies like Dark Web Solutions and Mys-toCrypto Web Services.

Both of those companies are no longer partners. And the editors and researchers I hired have all jumped ship to the Quintasm Contras. Now it's just me and my computer once again, like it was five years ago.

Jotham's betrayal has been the most difficult for me. Not only did he steal my email list, he turned on me and this newsletter in a way that I will never be able to understand.

I should note he was responsible for a lot of technological upgrades around here. His email analytics were so important to attracting sponsors like Bust The Central Bank Board Game and The Idiot's Guide To Taking On The Man. And I trusted him. He was my go-to guy for so many things, and now that he's gone I'm forced to learn a lot of techy components of this operation that I had never paid attention to.

It's difficult, but I won't let it break me.

Rest assured, my contempt for the Federal Reserve remains. I still think they operating a counterfeiting scam at the expense of the blue-collar worker.

Your support through the years, whether it was through email forwards or mentions on social media, filled me with pride. As the newsletter began to grow, my mental health showed significant improvement. I noticed my therapist's discomfort with my clear-eyed resolve when I told her that I could see the seeds of truth sprouting into revolutionary flowers. She told me that she had never seen me so full of purpose shortly before she told me she no longer felt comfortable treating me. Was it because I was crazy? No! It was because I was so focused that it scared her.

I'm not going to stop fighting and I'm not going to move back in with my parents.

This is my commitment to you all, my loyal subscribers. You have been heard. I am sorry that many of you have left but I am happy to have those that have stayed. The Hellfire Prophecy has shown me that I need to keep an open mind to all potential plots against humanity that are circulating.

I am currently working on some really fascinating content that is going to remind you all of why you subscribed in the first place.

This newsletter is not dead. Long live this newsletter.

Please stay tuned. Please.

Yours Truly,
Fed Up! Steve

## WITHERSPOON SIGHTING SPARKS SPECULATION

Man at farmer's market fitting Witherspoon description broke into sprint after individual called out his name.

## VIDEO CIRCULATING ONLINE
## WORRIES WITHERSPOON SUPPORTERS

Surveillance video at New Hampshire gun store suggests "radical provocateur" is preparing for battle. And paying for it with cash.

## WITHERSPOON VIRUS EXPOSES SCORES
## OF UNPROTECTED COMPUTERS

A downloaded video purports to tell Witherspoon's real story. The only thing real about it was the credit card theft.

## DISHEVELED MAN CONFIRMED
## TO BE WITHERSPOON

A New York Yankees hat couldn't keep the country's most sought-after hermit from being recognized at a New Hampshire liquor store.

# B/BOOK_OF_STROBE

**u/ RE@LITY_BITE$_420** - The Book of Strobe may not b totes accurate...My sources at the #DeepState tell me it's a distraction,,,The goal is 2 to make it seem too dum so everybody jus stops pointin fingers at the actual illuminati witherspoon clan

**SLORELORD6969** - Thats wut I keep sayin

**Fukitall** - ME 2!!!!!

**McRational McGee** - This whole witherspoon thing is so obviously a distraction. dont fall 4 it errbody. Its soooo stooopid. they arent the illuminati. Never hav been,. Why wont anybody see that!>!?!??!?

**P_OR_OUS)(MULTIVERSE)__!** - IN THIS TIMELINE OF REALITY WE ARE NOT GOING TO REALIZE THE HELL-FIRE PROPHECY. BUT IN OTHERS???? YES. THERE IS A TIMELINE FOR EVERYTHING

**McRational McGee** - THIS IS THE DUMBEST TIMELINE

**MITCHWITHERBLOGS** - RE@LITY_BITE$_420 – who do you know at the #deepstate

**RE@LITY_BITE$_420** - CANT divulg source

**MITCHWITHERBLOGS** - I need to know

**RE@LITY_BITE$_420** - U r not in the need to know category

**McRational McGee** - You r not in the need to know category either RE@LITY_BITE$_420. None of us r!!!!

**MITCHWITHERBLOGS** - RE@LITY_BITE$_420 I can help

**RE@LITY_BITE$_420** - Who are you?

**MITCHWITHERBLOGS** - Who do you think I am?

**RE@LITY_BITE$_420** - Im not playin that game

**MITCHWITHERBLOGS** - I CAN GET TO STROBE. I CAN HELP

**RE@LITY_BITE$_420** - ?????????

**Fukitall** - MITCH MFin WITHERSPOON IN DA HOUSE. WADDUP MITCHY! I BEEN FOLLOWIN U 4 a whil. THIS DUDE DA REAL DEAL YALL!

**MITCHWITHERBLOGS** - hi

**RE@LITY_BITE$_420** – this thread just got interestin

**P_OR_OUS)(MULTIVERSE)__!** – In this timeline are you for or against the resistance?

**MITCHWITHERBLOGS** – Im just someone doing their own research. Iv been in a dark place for a few days now. Its time 4 me to take back my life. Its time for me to stand up for myself. I hav nightmares about my grandpa standin over me tellin me to keep my mouth shut. I have nightmares about my dad pullin off his face to reveal a lizard head that shoots mind control lasers into my eyes. Im paranoid everywhere I go. I cant play video gamez. I cant surf the internet. I cant, you know, do private things. All the comments on my blogs are getting in my head. I need to know what is goin on with my fam. This is the first time I have said any of this to anyone.

**RE@LITY_BITE$_420** – DM me. I show you the way out of the funk.

**MITCHWITHERBLOGS** – How do I know you on the level? So many people tryin to scam me RN.

**McRational McGee** – DON'T LISTEN TO HIM. I CAN SHOW YOU WHATS UP. THESE PEOPLE ARE ALL SCAMMERS. THERE IS NO DEEP STATE. DM Me.

**RE@LITY_BITE$_420** – I got the receipts. Nobody can challenge these receipts. Nobody. The public internet isn't safe. I'll show you. A whole new world.

**P_OR_OUS)(MULTIVERSE)__** – I love that song.

**Fukitall** – A new fantastic point of view

No one to tell us no

Or where to go

Or say we're only dreaming

A whole new world

A dazzling place I never knew

But when I'm way up here

It's crystal clear

That now I'm in a whole new world with you

**RE@LITY_BITE$_420** – Mitch. You still there?

**McRational McGee** – He got smart and bailed. Im gonna help him understand it all away from all this nonsense.

**MITCHWITHERBLOGS** – Im here.

**RE@LITY_BITE$_420** – These sites aren't safe anymore. Theyre watching me type this. I'll show you what you need to know. DM me.

**McRational McGee** – Dm me!!!! These ppl DO NOT KNOW WHAT THEY R TALKIN ABOUT

# 72

# Journal Entry #2

I'm so bored.

It appears that not having the interaction option available to me has severely curtailed my enjoyment of alone time.

All the way back to my childhood, I remember watching others playing basketball or baseball outside and thinking to myself, *I'd rather be here, in my room.* It was in that room that I would ponder fantastical scenarios about my father, working deep undercover in the most dangerous places on Earth. He was no doubt blending into local communities and collecting information on bad guys, using sophisticated tricks of the spy trade, thus making the world safe for American boys like me.

Yesterday I tried meditating. Maybe that would help, I thought. Turns out, all I could see in my mind's eye was a group of smug assholes congratulating themselves for canceling me from society.

Perhaps they *should* congratulate themselves. I'm stuck in a putrid prison cell of my own making. I shouldn't be here.

People like me should be celebrated and rewarded for our curiosity, insights, and advancement of humanity. Without us, civilizational collapse is all but guaranteed. The idiots have taken over.

This thing, writing, it's turning against me. I need to sleep. I need a drink.

Perhaps my glimpse into true darkness is the end. And the beginning.

# 73

**From: Jotham ‹QUINTASMCONTRA1@substack.com›**
**To: FU Patriots**
**Subject: Contra Update**

Hola (Hi!),

Quick update on where we are at over here at Quintasm
Contra HQ. Lots of interesting (SECRET) stuff coming our
way from a number of Contras out there working the streets,
tracking the web, and recruiting new members. Our numbers
increase daily (by A LOT!). We have now become the most
trusted name in Quintasm prep. We got some partnerships
coming up with a few companies (BIG COMPANIES) that are
doing great stuff for the Quintprep community (CAMPING
EQUIPMENT, COMMUNICATIONS EQUIPMENT, MEALS,
GUNS, AMMO, etc.). Stay tuned. You do not want to be asleep
at the wheel (NOT CHECKING EMAIL) when we drop some of
this information. It's also gonna have some top-secret Strobe
updates (WHERE IS HE???) and some news from our Hellfire
Prophecy scholars (SMART FOLKS) who have been hard at
work deciphering some of the clues out there online and in
the Ivory tower libraries where all this planning goes down.

All of that is to say that things are really starting to gel (GO
WELL) over here at Quintasm Contra HQ. We're building up

our team (WE'RE HIRING!) and we're getting some great feedback (EMAILS, TWEETS, REDDIT SUBGROUPS, BLATHR BOMBS, 12CHAN JAMS) from you all, our faithful email subscribers.

I also wanted to take a second to respond to Fed Up! Steve's recent update. I know that in some of my early blasts I suggested that Fed Up! Steve wasn't exactly ride or die for the Contra movement (UNSUPPORTIVE). I still have my doubts, to be totally honest. But I also feel like Fed Up! Steve deserves to be treated with respect. You all that are going out there and hacking his bank accounts, spray painting his Ford Taurus with obscenities, maybe you should calm that stuff down (STOP).

Steve and I go way back. He gave me a chance after I got fired from my call center job for cursing out an old lady (SHE DESERVED IT) and when I got taken down for faking Percocet prescriptions. We may have had differing opinions on the Prophecy, and I may think that the Federal Reserve is just a symptom not the cause of all of the master manipu-lation in this world, but at the end of the day, Steve is an alright guy. And it seems like he has taken the success of the Contras hard (he sad). Which, to be honest, isn't really what I intended. I know I seceded from that group in a kind of flashy (GANGSTA) way, but man, I regret it a little. I coulda been less flashy (GANGSTA) and still got this email newsletter off the ground using my passion and my writing skills (ADMIT IT, YOU LOVE THE PARENTHESES!!!!!!).

So, Steve, if you're reading this, I appreciate what you did for me. I never woulda kicked those percs without you. Let's bury the hatchet. Let buy gunz be buy gunz (INSIDE JOKE BETWEEN STEVE AND ME). Your last email really hit me in the gut and I hope that you can see your way out of this sad (depressed) state and get back to doing what you do best. You will always be welcome here.

That's it for now. I promise the next email will focus on the Contra uprising.

Rise up,
QC Jotham

## WITHERSPOON RESTAURANT
## FOOTAGE RAISES QUESTIONS

An agitated man in a New York Yankees hat, claiming he is the "information messiah," disrupted diners at a New Hampshire Applebee's. After eating an elderly woman's french fries, pocketing her skirt steak, and consuming her margarita, he yelled, "Get ready!" and stormed out.

## WITHERSPOON SIGHTING SHOCKS RESIDENTS

A disheveled man fitting the description of Strobe Witherspoon ransacked a Cumberland Farms market in Keene, screaming "Viva la revolución" and making off with stationery supplies, camouflage clothing, and two bottles of Gatorade.

## HAS THE WITHERSPOON HIDEOUT BEEN
## UNCOVERED?

A cabin in the White Mountains of New Hampshire was raided by online detectives, revealing stacks of printouts about the Strobe Witherspoon story and empty bottles of Gatorade and Jack Daniel's. Witherspoon was nowhere to be found.

## ONE WEEK LATER, STILL NO STROBE

Hopes for Witherspoon's return dwindle as sightings stop.

# @FEDUP!STEVE

Tweet Storm

1/ I HAVE KIDNAPPED STAN HANK THE CHAIRMAN OF THE FEDERAL RESERVE BANK OF THE UNITED STATES

2/ THIS IS NOT A TEST #THEREALDEALHOLYFIELD

3/ REPEAT, THIS IS NOT A TEST #DONOTTESTME

4/ THE NEXT PHASE OF THE REVOLUTION BEGINS NOW #FEDUP!

5/ I HAVE TWO DEMANDS

6/ 1. CLOSE DOWN THE FED #ENDTHEFED

7/ 2. HAND OVER STROBE WITHERSPOON TO ME. HE WILL THEN BE TRIED FOR CRIMES AGAINST HUMANITY BY A JURY OF HIS PEERS (DM ME IF YOU WOULD LIKE TO BE ON THAT JURY) #DOWNWITHSTROBE

8/ LET THE TRUTH PRE-VALE

9/ IF STROBE IS INNOCENT LET HIM MAKE HIS CASE

10/ IF HE IS GUILTY OF MASTERMINDING THE FIFTH AND FINAL CYCLE OF THE HELLFIRE PROPHECY LET HIM PAY THE PRICE #HELLFIREPROPHECY

11/ THAT PRICE WILL BE DETERMINED BY THE QUINTASM CONTRAS, AS OVERSEEN BY MY FRIEND AND COMRADE @JOTHAMQCGANGSTA

12/ IF YOU ARE QUESTIONING THE VERACITY OF MY CLAIMS I HEREBY PRESENT YOU WITH A PICTURE OF STAN HANK NEXT TO A NEWSPAPER WITH TODAY'S DATE ON IT.

## WHERE IN THE WORLD IS STROBE WITHERSPOON?

With society in a freefall, one man may be the only thing standing between us and civilizational collapse.

## IS STROBE WITHERSPOON BEHIND GREATEST PRANK OF ALL TIME?

Has this misanthropic individual trolled the whole world?

## DOW HALTS TRADING AFTER FOURTH CONSECUTIVE SELLOFF

Major indexes are now below 1987 levels with no end in sight to this bear market.

## FED CHAIR IN GOOD SPIRITS DESPITE CAPTIVITY

Stan Hank posted on his twitter (@Shank1929) saying he missed his family but that he otherwise remains unharmed.

## SHOOTOUT AT GUN STORE OVER SHORTAGE

An armed gunman raided a gun store. There were multiple casualties.

# World Leaders Plead For Cooler Heads To Prevail

Central News Network

In an unprecedented move, the leaders of China, Saudi Arabia, Iran, France, Venezuela, Turkey, Russia, Israel, Argentina, Nigeria, Mexico, Kyrgyzstan, and South Korea released a joint statement addressing the "Hellfire situation." The full text is below.

> *A Message from the Unified Coalition of Countries (UCC)*
>
> We, the leaders of various countries, representing numerous religions, ethnicities, races, and political systems, come together in unity to plead for a resolution to the current state of unrest and uncertainty in the United States of America.
>
> It is incumbent upon us all as human beings to look past that which makes us different. We must understand that the international system under which the

United States of America is a significant contributor is fragile and must be treated with sincerity and grace.

A global coordinated response that transcends nation-state borders is therefore required.

As such, the UCC unanimously calls upon the various actors within the United States of America to enter into negotiations regarding the safe return of Stanley Hank, the chairman of the Federal Reserve System of the United States.

If we act now to bring Dr. Hank safely back from captivity, we can restore confidence in the global trading system.

We must address this issue in a manner that is inclusive and respectful.

In recognition of the conflicting narratives around this situation, we recommend the creation of an International Committee for the Study and Reconciliation of the Hellfire Prophecy (ICSRHP).

This committee will explore the role of the Witherspoon family in relation to the Hellfire Prophecy. It will endeavor to clear up misconceptions where relevant, but it will also seek to adjudicate any legitimate evidence of misdeeds. Upon its completion in three months' time, this committee will release an action plan for moving forward and achieving economic and social stability.

This is the first step toward healing that we hope the people of the United States of America, most specifically those that are agitating against the Federal Reserve and the Witherspoon family, will take. This will help return a sense of normalcy and protocol to an international system that is buckling under the weight of this unrest and is critical for the health and well-being of the human race.

# 78

# Everything Is Going Great, So We're Done

SPELUNKER

If you're reading this, then you still have access to the internet. Congrats. Thirty percent of the country's internet providers are now out of business, and people are digging up fiber-optic cables and selling them to Quintasm Contras for their private communications channels. Good times.

But this isn't about that. It's mostly just a note to say thank you for your support. The last few months have been challenging, to say the least. Apparently, this Strobe Witherspoon story that we have been doing our best to ignore just won't die. In fact, its continued takeover of every facet of society has been killing everything in its wake. Including this website.

Our parent company has officially shut its doors, and our lawyers have informed us that they own all the content and hardware in our cramped Bushwick office space. It's apparently going up for auction ASAP.

I guess it's fitting that our country's Crapitalist™ shackles proved too powerful for this fly-by-night operation full of obnoxious, overeducated castoffs. If Karl M was here, he would probably look at us with a smirk and say, "What'd you think was gonna happen? The workers never win." Thanks, Karl. Thanks a lot.

I always thought it would be the robots that did us in, but alas, some idiots with a Twitter account and a shaky relationship with the truth beat them to it.

As far as the content that lives on our servers is concerned, your guess is as good as mine. Maybe no one will bid on it. Is anybody really buying anything these days other than wood-burning stoves, cans of pinto beans, and AK-47s?

Me? I'll probably just go back to my parents' house in Chappaqua. They have a big fireplace and a stocked bunker full of canned goods that should get me through the coming winter. Turns out I probably shouldn't have mocked them for that doomsday bunker they built after the last crisis.

I should probably figure out what the eff to do with my life now that journalism is dead. Maybe grad school, if those exist after this thing blows over. Maybe I'll join the resistance. Ugh.

So, you know, good job everybody. It was fun while it lasted. Hope you had a laugh or learned a thing or two from us here at *Spelunker*. Perhaps we should have taken this debacle a little more seriously. Perhaps we shouldn't have focused so much on the Uighur genocide in China. Who knows.

*Dasvidaniya*, comrades. Stay warm.

# @STROBEWITHER

Tweet

I must take responsibility for my destiny. This circus must end. Words are not enough. Update forthcoming. :)

## NEWS OF WITHERSPOON RETURN SENDS MARKETS HIGHER

*Is this the end of the bear market?*

## WITHERSPOON TWEET SPARKS WAVES OF EXCITEMENT AND TREPIDATION

*Can he be trusted to right the ship?*

## THE TWEET THAT BROKE TWITTER, AND MAY HAVE SAVED US ALL

*Retweet record illustrates global fascination and apprehension over current crisis.*

# Twitter Direct Message

@derekblum --> @strobewither

Strobe! You may remember me from the panel that we were on about crisis communications and the Internet at the Aspen Institute a few years back. Seems like FOREVER ago. I'm done writing for the *New Patriot* and ready to help you with your communications apparatus. You're going to need all the help you can get. I can take this "Truther" revolution from rhetoric to reality. From Tweet strike to Tweet storm. Let's chat.

# @STROBEWITHER

Tweet Storm

1/ STROBE 2.0 IS UPON US

2/ I have come to the conclusion that all of the suffering I have experienced is in service of my larger calling

3/ I cannot deny this call to leadership

4/ Those who attack facts and civic discourse shall fall. Those who value truth will ascend to their rightful place in our society

5/ We are no longer able to hide our heads in the sand, or in our phones

6/ This battle will be fought in the real world

7/ There is no need for long screeds

8/ We must prevail with our bodies and minds

9/ Facts are not up for debate

10/ Strobe is truth

11/ Truth is power

12/ Strobe is power

13/ More details to come please retweet

# Twitter Direct Message

---

@mitchwitherspoon --> @strobewither

---

Dad,

I hope you read this. I know we've both been through a lot recently. I think I now understand your struggle better than ever before. I've seen things.

For a while I was living a life of blissful ignorance. The world was burning down around me and I was just posturing and talking into a camera while I was pretending to help. But now I know that living out loud is a lie. Technopia is a lie. Militant Buddhism is a lie. Women who promise to be with you forever are a lie. I was a willing participant in a mirage. I don't want to be naïve anymore. I want to help.

I want to clear the Witherspoon name.

I want to stop the manipulation of the truth.

I want to make amends.

I want to join your team.

# B/STROBE_CODE

BLATHR – SOCIAL MEDIA'S
ANNOYING STEPCHILD

**u/hellfproph** - FAM! DON'T FALL FOR THE @STROBE-WITHER TWEET STORM. THIS IS #STROBECODE, DESIGNED TO TRIGGER THEFINAL CHAPTER IN THE PROPHECY. THE BOOK OF STROBE MAKES NUMEROUS CODED REFERENCES TO THIS EXACT SCENARIO! STROBE IS NOT POWER! #RESIST #RESIST #RESIST

**FROM: Jotham ‹QUINTASMCONTRA1@substack.com›**
**To: OldFedupGroup**
**Subject: THE. REVOLUTION. IS. NOW.**

QC CONTRAS,

The time has come (NOW). Witherspoon's recent announcement (SIGNAL) is nothing short of #Strobecode (CODED
LANGUAGE). This is clear as day. The secret signals from
the Hellfire Prophecy are now being revealed in front of our
eyes (AND BRAINS).

When an apologist writer from the media elite Derek Blum
joins the TRUTHER movement as comms director, you know
that this is all a ruse (CHARADE). Blum is a washed up status
quo cheerleader. He is just trying to stay relevant (RICH)
by attaching himself to the effort to topple the Quintasm
Contras! (HEROES OF THIS STORY).

If we don't act now there'll be nothing left of our country. This
email is not safe. It's been infiltrated by agents of the Quintasm World Order (QWO). Assemble your supplies. Contact
your local Contra chapter for further instructions. There is no
tomorrow unless we act today.

**FROM: Fukitall Jones <fukitall@gmail.com>**
**TO: QC SE REGIONAL CHAPTER**
 **<QCSERC@compuserve.com>**
**SUBJECT: Im ready**

Dear Contra Regional Director,

Im writing 2 inquire about the upcoming revo. i been following along with the emails and the instructions. I hav been
distributing the approved memes to friends and family. I
await the next update with nervus excitement. I stockpiled
the recommended supplies and munitions. been doing
pushups and situps and walking two miles a day. I am in
the best shape of my life for the most important moment
of my life.

I jus wanted to say that I never felt motivated to do anything
like this before. This community is the future before joining
the contras I was nothing now I am standing on the right side
of history ready to have my voice heard.

Eagerly yours,
Sergeant Fukitall

## CONTRAS BRACE FOR BATTLE AGAINST WITHERSPOON SUPPORTERS

Armed militias are having their moment

## FATE OF FED CHAIRMAN REMAINS UNCERTAIN

Rumors of his demise may have been exaggerated

## US DOLLAR COLLAPSES IN EARLY MORNING TRADING

Gold standard formally adopted by
governments around the world

## PROPHECY OF SOCIETAL COLLAPSE APPEARS TO BE SELF-FULFILLING

Hysterical is now the new normal

## NON-PERISHABLE GOODS BECOME US CURRENCY

Canned and dried food scarce as global
supply chain breaks down

## #TRUTHERS ORGANIZE TO SUPPORT WITHERSPOON

But will their arsenals be any match
for the Quintasm Contras?

# Mitch Witherspoon Vlog 2435

Transcript

**MW:** Mitch Witherspoon here with a special update. From my dad. I reached out to him on Twitter. We reconciled. We both have been goin through a lot these days. I know I said no more vlogs. But he insisted. Father son role reversal! Just me and him, alone in this storage room. I will take a step back and let him talk to y'all. He's got an update on the revolution. Take it from here Dad.

[PHONE CAMERA SPINS AROUND]

[A BEARDED STROBE WITHERSPOON SITS BEHIND A DESK]

**SW:** we ready? You got this?

**MW:** I got this, go ahead.

**SW:** Thank you Mitch. I appreciate it

**MW:** I know.

**SW:** It's good to see you.

**MW:** You too dad, please we don't have time.

**SW:** Ladies and gentlemen of the world, supporters of truth and civility, stewards of Western civilization and beyond, and, I guess, subscribers to Mitch's travel channel: I come to you today with the most important of updates. The so-called Contras out there are crusaders alright, crusaders for anarchic stupidity, troll-faced shitposters of ill repute with no ability to distinguish reality from their video game infused half-ironic computer bubble of absurdity. That crusade deserves to be crushed by the weight of its idiotic and attention-starved puerility.

[STROBE TAKES A DRINK FROM A GATORADE BOTTLE]

Handing myself over to that Fed UP or Contra movement or whatever they're calling themselves would be akin to accepting the end of American greatness. I reject this scenario. I will not be used as a pawn in some misguided extortion plot.

I also refuse to run.

Spending time alone by myself these past few months has made me realize things.

I must lead.

Call me the truth messiah if you must, but my crusade is not built on false prophets and false profits. It is the purest of pursuits for which defeat is not an option.

Those who join us, TRUTHERS, are destined to join the ranks of the evolutionary victors.

Those who fight us will be destined to the dustbin of history.

Already, in the early stages of my revolution, I have seen wonderful seeds of truth begin to flower. People from all different ideological backgrounds have joined forces to restore accuracy and decency to our national discourse.

To others out there, it's not too late to join. We need all of the help we can get. Human stupidity is a worthy foe. I have been fighting it for many years using my pen. That era is over. Now is the time for action, which is why I am no longer delivering these messages via the written word. Only my voice and the visual demonstration of my resolve and certainty can vanquish this foe.

I shall not be defeated. We must band together to overwhelm the stupidity virus, flush it from our system, and inoculate ourselves from future outbreaks.

Luckily, our foes are, in fact, stupid. So we have that advantage. I am calling on all of my Truther brothers and sisters to follow my lead, procure the necessary firearms and other related military gear, and begin to establish strategic strongholds in your neighborhood. Ally yourself with other like-minded neighborhoods and wait for further guidance from central command.

Peace through truth will be our north star.

Those that follow me will ascend to the natural throne of enlightenment. From there we will transition to the most powerful weapons known to man—logic, reason, and honesty.

[LOUD BANG]

[BLOOD EMERGES FROM STROBE'S CHEST]

[MITCH WITHERSPOON TURNS THE PHONE CAMERA ON HIMSELF]

MW: Trust in what you believe not what you see for too long I was an unwitting agent of this type of visual deception even as I tried to free myself from it.

My father did not understand his role in the indoctrination machine so I took it upon myself to short circuit him the TRUTHER movement is a false quest for dominance and a return to the status quo that must be rejected destroy your creator trust no one that doubts the superiority of this vision.

My eyes are open.

Are yours?

Mitch out.

[OFF CAMERA SOUNDS OF DOOR GETTING KICKED IN]

[CAMERA SHUTS OFF]

# 89

# Chapter 8: My Mother's Daughter

As I reflect on my life story, from humble Slovakian beginnings to a place at the table alongside the most powerful political and economic elites of my generation, I can't help but shed a tear for those who sacrificed so much for me to reach those heights. I am thinking first and foremost of my mother, Anichka.

Her name translates to "compassion." Anichka didn't ask for much, but she sacrificed bigly. She did it with grace and, yes, compassion.

Sometimes, in retrospect, I wish maybe she hadn't demonstrated so much compassion. When my father would go out for one of his many "business dinners," she didn't complain. She continued working on the payroll ledgers, or filling out government forms, or putting new floor plans together for the next café.

He came home smelling like things other than business. Fruity smells mixed with stale beer and sweat. My sister whispered to me what those smells were as we lay awake in bed, listening to another late-night tirade. I still don't like fruity perfumes because of that.

He was always mad at her. Accusing her of not providing him with the support he needed to operate a successful business. Claiming she was not working hard enough, completely oblivious to his own delinquent behavior: sleeping well into the afternoon, failing to understand even the most fundamental components of the world wide web, and yes, failing to adhere to the building codes that would ultimately contribute to the death of my big sister.

Anichka's compassion never wavered. She mourned the death of her oldest daughter privately. She kept the business running as her husband sank deeper into depression and denial.

"You think some modeling agency is going to want you?" he asked, looking me up and down. "Not with that hair and that stomach," said the bald man with a paunch the size of a football (AKA soccer ball).

Desperate for his approval, I would show him pictures of Paulina Poriskova. "You look too similar to her," he said. "What does the modeling world need with someone else from this part of the world? Besides, she's connected to the Tajná Společnost. That's how she *really* got discovered."

The "TS" was supposedly a secret group that made all of the big decisions in the former Czechoslovakia and were still active in post-independence Slovakia. They were allegedly closely aligned with Soviet government leaders, many of whom had transitioned to "businessmen" after the fall of the Iron Curtain.

My father had become obsessed with these types of secret groups after my sister's death. It was their fault, he told us. He had books that he swore laid it all out. He had new friends who sat around smoking cigars and complaining about how "those people" had kept them from accumulating the fortune that seemed to be rightfully theirs. He was energized during his lectures to us about such things. He had found something to explain away his own misfortune that didn't include self-reflection. I found it naïve, but also harmless. He found it vindicating and exciting.

My mother, however, was showing signs of exhaustion. Her arthritis was getting worse. The work was breaking her. So much new technology to learn and buy and set up at the cafés. All while her business partner/husband continued to recede from view and dive deeper into his stories about government control of the levers of power.

I think she would have left him, had I not left first. I was her rock, I told myself, during those difficult times after Petra's death. But the modeling agency came calling, and I answered. I abandoned ship, leaving my mother with only her work to sustain and distract her. She knew she wouldn't keep the business if she left him. That kind of thing wasn't acceptable in Slovakia during that time.

My father was too proud to ask me to help them emigrate, and my mother was probably afraid that it would make him mad if she brought it up.

But I could tell. During our weekly phone calls, she seemed to be increasingly interested in American culture and my life in New York City. Also, by that time, the internet café business was on its way out.

Dominik was no longer drinking much or staying out late. He wasn't doing much of anything, as it were, other than surfing the internet. Feeding his conspiratorial appetite. The irony of it all—his discovery of the internet just at the point when it was of no use for the business—did not help matters.

I told my father that it was my dream to have them join me and experience the wonders of America the way I had. That was a lie. It was my dream to help my mother find some solace. Find some relief from an existence that had become too difficult for me to bear: one daughter gone, the other gone away, and a husband who refused to take any responsibility. I may have left my mother for fifteen years, going out and focusing on my own career, my own success, my own journey. But I never forgot what she did for me.

I started the process without even telling them. Then, on a trip back to Bratislava, I asked Anichka—alone—whether she had ever thought about it. She shrugged her shoulders. "Sometimes," she said. "But it's such a hassle. All the paperwork. And your father ..." She trailed off.

"What if I told you it wasn't a hassle? I'll take care of it. We'll use the appropriate legal channels."

"You think your father will be open to it?" she asked.

"Who cares?"

"*Moje diet'a!*" she said. *My child* was what she would call me when I said something that offended her more traditional sensibilities.

"I'm serious," I told her. "If he doesn't want to come, he can stay."

She looked at me. I could tell that this scenario appealed to her.

Turns out, he did want to come. When we brought the idea to him, he shrugged his shoulders in a way that was intended to appear nonchalant but actually conveyed a sense of insecure excitement. When I told him that I could take care of most of the paperwork with the team of lawyers that we had on retainer back home, his shrug turned into a soft nod. "Sounds good," he said.

We had the best lawyers. They could speed up the process, through the appropriate legal channels, and get it all squared away in under eight months. Some people were surprised by that speed because of the regulations around that type of immigration that had just made their way through Congress. "Those new rules are designed to keep people from coming in for the wrong reasons. Your parents want in for the right reasons. America welcomes them," my lawyer told me.

Getting them to the front of the line was the easy part. Getting them set up in New York in a way that prevented a return to my father's abusive ways was harder. I knew there was a good man in there somewhere. That man had been sideswiped by tragedy, and it was taking him to some dark places. A change of pace could be just what he needed, I told myself.

I was right!

I would not, however, have thought that Greek food would have been the secret ingredient. When the Greek owners of the restaurant in their neighborhood in Queens told them they were looking to retire, my mother asked me for a loan so they could buy the restaurant.

When I inquired about giving my parents the loan from money I had in my account, he scoffed. "Your parents?" he said. "They're never gonna pay you back. Slovaks running a Greek restaurant? Who wants that? This is why I keep you away from our finances."

I smiled. And gave my parents the money.

When they opened their third restaurant in Queens, he seemed unimpressed. "That's great, but come talk to me when they have success in Manhattan," he said.

He pouted all the way through that opening night party. Something about spending time in Queens made him uncomfortable.

Through it all, there was Anichka. Running another successful business venture in a country she barely knew, for a cuisine that was not her own. Seeing her thrive brought me so much joy. My eyes are tearing up as I write this.

My father was happy to play second fiddle to his wife by this point. He was moving slower, and he lacked the necessary culinary enthusiasm to be very useful in that department.

He still liked to hold court, building up a not-so-small coterie of elderly friends of various European and Asian descent, who would spend many hours at the first restaurant, drinking tea and talking about football (AKA soccer). That community was a godsend. All of the talk about politics and secret societies took a back seat to discussions of sports, music, and family.

Anichka kept the restaurants going for five more years after Dominik died. When cancer came calling for her, she didn't complain. She didn't want to be a bother. She dealt with it the way she had always dealt with it. With grace. And compassion.

She ended up better off than many other Slovaks she grew up with, so she never felt like she had the right to complain. She picked up the slack for other people in her family who were not as compassionate as her—my father, me.

She never seemed to hold it against me that I left her. I held it against me.

I'm never going to see my mother again in this world. I'm never going to see her small hands working the cash register and talking on the phone while directing a Mexican delivery boy—with just a head nod—to stop dilly-dallying and get on his bike with the boxed-up food that was getting cold on the counter.

But we will see each other again. This I know. And I will thank her for everything. Even if she doesn't want to hear it. Because she's the best.

I love you, Mom.

# 90

# OOF: A Compendium

Epilogue

**Editor's Note:** *We have reached the end of this compendium. Congratulations to those who made it this far. Or should I say condolences? Some of those last few chapters were difficult for me to organize, seeing as how every time I sat down to work on them, I was reminded of just how stupid it all became.*

*But I persisted, for posterity. And for you, dear reader.*

*While putting this book together, I frequently tried to put myself in your shoes. Were you coming across all this information for the first time? Or is this book a reminder of an era in American history that you are all too familiar with?*

*Perhaps you are sitting on a camping chair next to your tent, many decades later, warming your hands by the fire and keeping watch for predators—human and nonhuman alike. This book, dog-eared and pored over by hundreds of others in a post-American tribal outpost somewhere in the hinterlands of a once-great country, is used to educate children about the time just before "the demise."*

*Maybe you are reading this on an illegal internet connection at a secret library in one of the few remaining areas in the US not controlled by the Contras. In this scenario, the Contras ascended to great power on the heels of Mitch Witherspoon's act of surprising familial aggression. Mitch was handed a lofty position in the new government and proceeded to demonize and expel the Truthers from much of the United States. But the Truther rebels were able to maintain a handful of strongholds scattered across the great plains—AKA the "Free Zones"—and avoid the "content moderation" efforts of their would-be information overlords.*

*The story of Strobe Witherspoon is well known outside of the US and in the Free Zones. But any trace of this book within the "Great Firewall of America" is quickly erased. Here, the story of Strobe is told mostly through verbal storytelling and folklore. Anyone caught even uttering Strobe's name in the presence of Mitch is executed. On the other side of the firewall, in the Free Zones, the story of Strobe offers a small but notable shred of inspiration to a community of intellectual castoffs as they work to preserve the ideas and sensibilities of a country they no longer recognize.*

*Or maybe, just maybe, you are sitting in a comfortable chair, in a secure, pleasantly acclimatized home library. The room is softly lit, smooth jazz is emanating from the ceiling speakers, and you are flipping through this compendium on some electronic device of the future (maybe a hologram?). The story of Strobe, for you, is an amusing footnote in the story of America. A historical hiccup, when everybody got real dumb for a moment. But humanity found a way out and resolved the "great crisis of communication." In this scenario,* OOF: A Compendium *preserves the narrative fidelity of this story and is occasionally used by historians and policymakers of the future to warn against similar indiscretions.*

*For those living in this last scenario, the forthcoming reveal will likely be of little surprise. But here goes ...*

I am Strobe Witherspoon.

Everything in this compendium is true.

Except the "Editor" part. That was a literary flourish. I hope you, dear reader, will grant me a modicum of artistic license on that front.

If you didn't know already, my son did in fact shoot me and leave me for dead in the Somerville Dunkin' storage room. And I have the chest scar and intestinal dysfunction to prove it. Lucky for me, he was not a good shot. And thanks to a small group of dedicated Truthers, I was able to escape and recuperate in an undisclosed location. Mitch was, however, successful in shooting and killing Derek Blum and two Truther guards on the way out. RIP Finbar and Jeff. Sorry I never learned your last names.

I started working on this book during my solitary confinement in the White Mountains of New Hampshire during my first "forced hiatus" from human interaction. But I got sidetracked by my plans for Strobe 2.0—aka my short-lived dance with revolutionary leadership. What an idiot I was.

The alcoholism and violent outbursts that marked the years after Wheeler's death made an ignominious encore. My journal entries from that time offer hints of this breakdown, of a man alone with his thoughts, unable to manage his anger and remain on the periphery of societal breakdown. Not even my attempt to distract myself by penning a new chapter of *FLOTUS* could keep me from crumbling. In fact, that chapter,

in which I not-so-subtly grapple with my mother's unwavering selflessness, only served to magnify my mania and sense
of anxious isolation.

That isolation created a savior complex of almost incal-
culable hubris. Alas, that phase was violently, and quickly,
squashed. Not by some random radical miscreant but by
someone in possession of a significant amount of my DNA.

Much of Mitchell's radicalization happened in plain sight,
for all of his followers to see. Opportunists took advantage of
the vulnerability that many young men his age feel. I could not
track down evidence of that move from the web to the dark
web, but I don't think I need to see it to understand it. Hateful
and unhinged misinformation combined with Mitch's deep-
seated (and justified) anger toward me, created a powerful
counterweight to my own megalomania. How fitting.

My son's betrayal was the final straw. The final humiliation
for me, Strobe Witherspoon, a person who made his living
reveling in the seemingly endless entertainment value of other
people's humiliation. Mitch's turn to the dark side convinced
me that male Witherspoon DNA had no place in society.

I do not plan to return this time. I no longer wish to mine
the underbelly of human behavior for the entertainment
of others. I am not kidding. As such, I have instructed my
Truther benefactors to keep me in the dark regarding the situation in America.

I was also not kidding when I said in the prologue that
Strobe was gone. Being the Editor allowed me to step away
from Strobe. I was able to include the less savory elements of
my former life in this book from a somewhat detached place.

The Editor helped me communicate one other thing:
we are all unreliable narrators. I was able to direct my story
and, in some cases, misdirect it, for the greater purpose of

maintaining the reader's interest and communicating larger truths in a more compelling manner than otherwise would have been possible.

Alas, this may all be in vain, since it is only the victors who get to write history. As of the time of this writing, I do not know who the victors are. The Contras and their ilk may have a story that's more exciting, or more persuasive, or simpler, or more in line with the story that people want to hear.

My story, it seems, is none of those things. I did not become the leader of a truth revolution.

With this book, I am, however, able to wage a small battle for the reclamation of the Strobe Witherspoon narrative. Only those who are reading this, in whatever future scenario they inhabit, can make an assessment regarding the outcome of this battle.

TL;DR: bias never dies; it just convinces you that it doesn't exist. The Editor was a plot device to demonstrate this point.

Did it work? Did I win the battle?

Are you slightly better protected from future efforts of bad faith narrative sculpting?

Or do you, dear reader (from whichever future timeline you occupy), find yourself thinking that this exercise is just as misguided and hypocritical as the efforts of those I attack, proving further the impossible task of determining truth from a potpourri of biased storytelling and self-interest? Perhaps you find this book to be a frustrating exercise in spastic meta-misdirection and unfocused hubris from a washed-up author of yesteryear with very little to offer other than unbridled misanthropy and literary gimmickry. Or, even worse, you think that this is a work of little contemporary relevance because you live in a world so far removed from mine that historical artifacts such as this book possess no present value for you.

Everyone you know believes that narratives can and should contain whatever information is necessary to further one's own interests. Everything is subjective, and facts are an illusion. Propaganda = Truth.

But I will say to those of you who hold any or all of the opinions put forth in the above paragraph: at least you made it this far; at least you're engaging with the material. Which, quite frankly, is better than nobody reading this book at all. That would be the worst scenario.

I am in occasional contact with other Truthers through a complex labyrinth of intermediaries, but none of them know my exact whereabouts. They have been tasked with publishing this book, which I now occasionally refer to as *The Real Book of Strobe*.

In closing, don't try to find me. In the world I now inhabit, tyrannical government is real, and reason does NOT beat guns. Guns beat guns. I have a formidable stockpile. Much of my day is spent cleaning, fixing, shooting, and organizing my collection. These activities are my lifeblood, my new addiction, my literal defense mechanisms that protect me from bad guys and help me avoid contact with the world I once inhabited. My ammunition-making skills are strong. My property is sufficiently booby-trapped for anybody who doesn't believe me. Heed my warning: my aim is better than my son's.

One final sales pitch: if there is still a currency system in place that allows items such as this to be purchased, please do so. Truthers could probably use the money. I know it's not much. But it's all I can offer. I wish it had a better ending.

The End

Made in the USA
Coppell, TX
14 April 2021